black and white home, The Ancient House, Little Stretton, near Church Stretton, Mrs. Caradoc Evans, widow of the famous Welsh writer, publishes on Monday her 44th book as Countess Barcynska—"I was shown heaven." A few weeks ago she published her 67th book as Oliver Sandys.—"The poppy and the rose." Both books are set in Shropshire. "The poppy and the rose" tells the story of a girl who takes a job in a girls' school in the county, and "I was shown heaven" deals with the fortunes of a repertory company.

Smile in the Mirror

FRIEDA BLOCH, 35 and an inter-national stage and film star, relates her life story to a journalist, Gerard Hemming, who has visited her to interview her for television.

She tells of how her father died in Dachau, how she danced, was injured, and fell in love. After her husband was tragically killed, she took small parts in films – and was later swept into Hollywood's glamorous life. Then she met Teddie Hamilton. . . .

The story of those romantic years, before Frieda resolves to 'smile in the mirror' and face the future with an open heart, is very moving, and Countess Barcynska tells it with an insight and a compassion which will delight all her readers.

COUNTESS BARCYNSKA

Smile in the Mirror

HURST & BLACKETT

HURST & BLACKETT LIMITED
178-202 Great Portland Street, London, W.1.

AN IMPRINT OF THE   HUTCHINSON GROUP

London Melbourne Sydney
Auckland Bombay Toronto
Johannesburg New York

★

First published 1963

*This book has been set in the Baskerville type face.
It has been printed in Great Britain on Antique
Wove paper by Cheltenham Press Ltd., Cheltenham.*

For
NANCY van der Veen
With Love

'I HAVE an appointment with Miss Frieda Corbett.'

Gerard Hemming, book-critic and feature-writer for top circulation newspaper the *Daily Flight*, celebrated interviewer of topical personalities on television, slid his card across the West End hotel reception counter.

The commissionaire picked it up, glanced at it and reacted immediately.

'One moment, sir.' He connected himself with a VIP suite number on the switchboard, announced the name of the visitor and received his reply. 'Very good, madam. He will be with you immediately.' Calling one of the hotel messengers: 'Show this gentleman up to Suite 125.'

The caller found himself duly escorted from the first stop of the lift along the softly pile-carpeted corridors to the suite now occupied by the recently arrived international star, both of stage and films, who had come over from America to make a brief appearance in London in an imported Transatlantic success. Musicals, straight, every facet of show business, this amazing creature seemed to have at her finger-tips.

His main interest was to ascertain how, and by what means, she had proceeded so far and to such heights when so comparatively little was known about her. Unlike most of the effulgent in the world of entertainment, except for the traditionally aloof Greta Garbo, the sex-life and marital excursions, if any, of Frieda Corbett had never been publicised; and the news-hounds and gossip-writers had never been given, nor had they been apparently able to glean any of the customary salacious tit-bits of information for their mixed bag of Names that spell News.

What was he likely to discover concerning her? Except that he had his commission to carry through and hers was the current titillating personality with whom a television talk had been requested, he wasn't at all keen on this preliminary interview. At his present age of thirty-eight he had been journalising in the Street of Ink for seventeen years and succeeded beyond his expectations.

In addition, his particular flair as television interviewer was due to his glancing mind and quick grasp of essentials, an eye which he could swivel with telescopic accuracy upon whatsoever star he had to focus, plus a disarmingly friendly method of approach and a persuasively well-modulated voice which very often lured his unsuspecting victims into the web and led them to reveal themselves very often as suddenly and unwittingly as an entangled fly.

He was disposed to be cynical of most theatrical personalities, an attitude of mind not only engendered by his journalistic and television interviews with such, but because, psychologically, it went back much further than that. His early background had been theatrical on both sides and, a lonely only son, his boyhood in holiday time had been spent between two sets of parents (divorced and remarried). He had been public school and university educated before he had embarked upon his self-chosen profession, and eventually found that he could excel. He had also written a best-seller on public school life which had been much discussed and aligned as an important and outspoken factual document upon adolescent life although in the form of fiction. His television appearances (seated with the back of his head and shoulders only visible to viewers) had multiplied his reputation far beyound newspaper range. In this respect his expertise had frequently been misdescribed. He was no deliberate, ruthless inquisitor. By nature he was forthright and direct, but fundamentally kind except when in certain instances palpable insincerity and calculated exhibitionism annoyed him.

The same held true of stage plays and players of the ultra-modern school, not only of the kitchen sink variety, angry young men or the purposely intellectual question-mark abstruse. He could never bring himself to excuse or praise performances in which sloppy deportment was all that was offered to a public who had paid for its seats hoping for something different. In trenchant terms he deplored the appearances of so many socialité debs 'inflicting themselves upon boards which squeaked in agony more often than not, and with no more talent than a grain of Epsom Salts.' There had recently been published an exceedingly forthright article he had written for an equally forthright weekly periodical with a policy and outlook as vigorous and fearless as his own. He had put the blame, amongst others, upon rich Daddy from the Midlands who could afford to be a backer and 'an angel,' as such are known, or rich 'Uncle' Mr. Lotsocash, and also the astute and expensive publicity agent who knew all the ropes.

His slashing criticism had ended:

'Unfortunately, folk like the public who pay for what they hoped was going to be entertainment, and critics like myself, find ourselves sitting in the stalls to be bored to death or driven to the theatre bar by this kind of fare. Or to see and hear the words of the Bard spoken mincingly by young men of doubtful sex. Oh, God, put back thy universe and give me John Barrymore! Give me Tod Slaughter and

9

yesterday. As that great poet of France wrote: "Where are the snows of yesteryear?" Alas, Francois Villon, they are melted. So has the British stage. Tonight I shall throw my dusty cloak around my shoulders, for I am going out, but not to the theatre. I go to the grocers and I am going to buy myself some good ham.'

His stinging article had been noted and quoted, and especially it had not pleased many self-satisfied members of the profession; but Gerard Hemming had reached that stage when, following in the footsteps of the late James Agate, he was not afraid to say or write what he truly thought without fear or favour.

So, of course, Frieda Corbett would probably be prepared for him and on her guard. This was only an excursionary interview before the one to be televised was even agreed upon. He had to persuade her about that, if she needed persuading, which he very much doubted.

The hotel attendant opened the door of Suite No. 125 with his pass-key, leading into a small hall, knocked upon the inner door, stood aside announcing the caller, and withdrew.

Gerard Hemming entered the flower-filled lounge.

2

THE full sunshine of a belated capricious Spring was at that moment streaming in through the open window. A soft breeze was gently fluttering the muslin curtains and circulating the perfume from the profusion of mauve and deep purple lilac in vases all around. No other flowers. Lilacs only.

Thereafter, in his mind, Gerard Hemming always associated the name of Frieda with the sight and fragrance of lilac blooms, flowers with a scent so delicate that a breath of sanctity and spirituality seemed to be wafted from them, reminding him of the faint hallowed smell of lingering incense in the churches of Rome.

The first glimpse he had of her was a small figure standing before the gilt mirror over the mantelpiece, wearing a simple, short-jacketed, light tailored suit with a sailor collar. The rays of sunshine burnished her wavy, un-stylised copper hair which fell to her shoulders, heightening and illuminating it like a nimbus. She was leaning forward. He could only glimpse her reflection, but even so it was with a startled amazement at beholding again one whom he had seen for a few fleeting moments seventeen years ago in an insignificant bit-part on a film-set of an Austrian beer-garden set amongst lilacs and cherry trees with striped garden unbrellas over small tables. Seen, but never forgotten, because she, in the dress of a German peasant girl waitress, with velvet bodice, flounced full skirt and stiffened lace head-dress, had epitomized Mendelssohn's 'Spring Song' as she flitted between the tables on tiny feet so lightly stepping that they scarcely seemed to touch the grass.

Women had scarcely figured in his life up to now. In the heart of some men there is set a white velvet-lined shrine to be one day occupied by the image of a best-loved, or else to remain empty, never to be substituted for the false or the ephemeral.

Although she must have been in London on various occasions and there had also been film premières in which she had been the star, it had so happened he had never seen her upon the stage or screen. Except that she was famous, her name had no special interest or significance for him. He believed he had read somewhere she was of Continental origin, and so Corbett was probably her stage or married name.

As the attendant announced him, she had been intent upon performing a certain curious action, pressing the corners of her lips upward with each forefinger, and so smiling into the mirror. Putting the smile there, as it were.

Then swiftly as the door of the lounge was closed and she was alone with the interviewer, she turned to greet him, and so now he saw her face to face and knew without any doubt that this was no striking resemblance to the so-young girl he had seen seventeen years ago flitting in that short bit-part scene amongst the cherry and lilac trees in the Austrian beer-garden scene. Seventeen years had intervened and here was the woman.

His heartbeats hastened. He was aware of the fluttering of Fate's wings.

The smile on her lips was the loveliest thing, as lovely as she herself. The years seemed scarcely to have touched her.

The nimbus created by the sunshine was still around her head. Her heart-shaped little face was untouched by any artificial beauty aids, her complexion delicate, almost lily-ish, except for an over-bright spot of colour high on the cheekbones. Her eyes were a most unusual combination of green and blue.

Frieda!

He wanted to speak her name aloud as one gladly greets someone dearly loved after a long journey. The projected television interview he had come to propose and discuss with her was not in his thoughts at all in those magical moments.

The sea-green sapphire eyes, as deeply perceptive as his own with the instantaneous vision of the impressionist, took in their flash-shot of the man before her. In that enchanting Austrian film-set bit-part scene she had been so full of girlish delight and abandon in finding herself recapturing the fleeting moments of a romantic care-free childhood that she had been entirely oblivious of lookers-on. She had not even heard the raised clipped voice of the producer issuing instructions to this one and that.

Gerard Hemming. Of course she knew the name. He was the personality-plus interlocutor who, if such a thing had been possible as to make a slug converse, would have been able to infuse such a form of communication that would have been dissociated with its invertebrate nature.

How did he appear to her?

Tall, loosely-made, rugged, craggy-featured, clean-shaven. She liked his hair. It wasn't parted or waved, overlong or barber-contrived. It was dark brown, sprinkled with grey, slightly shaggy and grew strongly like goat's hair.

She liked him even before he had spoken. She was conscious of something that was flowing between them on

13

wave-lengths as it were, but the television interview he had come to talk over and persuade her to give – no, most certainly not for her. She had made her decision before she had confirmed the appointment for him to call upon her. Nor was she going to lead him up the garden path about that, or pretend she might be procurable for a higher fee than usual. She made that clear at once.

'Sit down, do, and let us talk, but not for any purpose of publicity. You will respect what I say? I think I do not need to ask. I have never met you before, but I have that confidential feeling which is most calming to a person of my nature. No, thanks, I do not smoke, but please light up yourself.'

Gerard lit a cigarette.

'Actually we have met before.'

The sea-green eyes widened.

'When was that? I have an almost royal memory for faces. It is the only royal thing about me who am just an ordinary person of the professional class who are entertainers, so it is in my blood. I do not think I should forget you even if you were in a crowd, if you were near enough for me to see.'

He told her.

'I was very near to you for a few moments, but you were not looking my way. You were entirely taken up with what you were doing.'

'And what was that?'

'Seventeen years ago down at the Ace Film Studios at Elstree. The scene was an Austrian beer-garden, a most realistic set, and the picture was called "Born Smiling". That was how you looked as you danced around between the tables filling tankards, and you were dressed in a peasant girl costume with a full bunchy skirt, muslin embroidered blouse, black velvet bodice and stiffened lace headdress with floating ribbons. I had been sent down by the newspaper I was working for at that time to do a tour of the studios and the Chairman was showing me around. Then I had to go back again with him to his office to collect some more information on their general programme and policy. When I had finished talking to him the studio was closing up for the day. I hung around the building and the gardens outside hoping to catch a glimpse of you, to come up and speak to you somehow. I looked into the studio café where late teas were being served. I waited outside the entrance gates on the look-out amongst those who were not driving away in cars, but I never caught another glimpse of you.'

'And yet all these years you have remembered me! How strange that you should!'

'Not so strange. I have wondered since so often what had happened to you over the years. I couldn't forget you, perhaps because I didn't want to forget.'

The sapphire eyes were shining.

'And so now we meet not altogether as strangers, even though on the set I did not perceive you, your interest in me which you have expressed is like a little golden thread that has been woven into some kind of a pattern in this tapestry of life. So speak, as you feel, and ask me what you like. You have come at the right moment. I am brimming over, and I have wanted to unbutton my lips. What matters to you and to me at this moment is the truth. Truth is better than gold. Face to face, as we are now, the truth comes out. I will talk to you of all that has been my life, filling in the tapestry for you, and you may forget it, or record it if you wish to, if it will give you any satisfaction to write my biography for some later date. Then I would also be satisfied because you would make it full and frank and true.

For that I would give you permission, and for me what a relief to speak and to spill the memories out of my heart! Shall we converse and commune in that manner? I am German-Polish by origin. My education is imperfect and sometimes speech becomes twisted and peculiar when I am in a hurry to express myself. So you must translate me and correct my twisted sentences. I will stick to the truth always. Neitsche, the philosopher, he said this: "In the mountains of truth you never climb in vain". So we should all be climbers, helping and pulling each other by the ropes of truth. And of you – will you speak of yourself first to me and fill in these gaps? Have you a wife, have you a home, have you some dear little children?'

'None of those, but I have my work and that makes me content when I am doing it – at least when I have my pen in my hand and I am writing what I like.'

'You do not always like what you write?'

'Very frequently not. Only when I write poetry.'

'Poetry? But are your poems published? In some other name perhaps?'

'Unpublished. Just a form of expression when it comes over me and I have to stand still and write wherever I am – on the edge of a pavement, or in a pub, or in the country, or by the sea when I can manage to get out of London.'

'One day you will speak a poem to me, or give it to me to read or let me speak it in the quiet, your words and your thoughts with my voice. Yes, please?'

'Then it would be set to music. Now, do you feel like telling me your own story?'

'I will make a commencement from my first rememberings. Move your chair a little closer towards the table with the vase of lilacs.' He did so. 'Now, do you see the leather photograph frame beside it? I keep it closed to prevent it

16

from fading. Wherever I go I take it with me. Open it, please.'

'May I?'

Gerard took up the small frame.

What he now looked upon was the grotesque photograph of a white chalked face, bald-pated with short black tufts of plaited hair in twists, a spread false nose, elongated black eyebrows and black-ringed eyes, and vastly exaggerated lips painted in a grin. It was the face of a clown.

3

'THAT was my father, the famous clown Nemo as he was known to the world, the Punchinello, the *auguste*, loved by one and all, but especially by children whom he also adored. He was never happier than when he was with children. In his heart, yes, to the last he was a child himself. Nemo Bloch – that was his name. Polish-German-Jewish blood in his veins. Yes, I am proud of the mixture, all three. It was Hitler who hated the Jews until their presecution became part of his madness manifesting itself even before the ravages of war and hatred had spread like a scourge amongst his partisans and adherents until they all became infected, and the four horses of the Apocalypse rushed out of their stable with their wild riders. Devastation, starvation, disease, torture, miseries and death, my friend.

'Death! When it was meant for us to live this life, to give, to love, to be friends, to wish to sing, to dance with the grace and the verve, abandon and control of the ballet dancers; to savour existence upon the stage of life illuminated by the footlights of intelligence and the pilot-light from above, never to despair. I do not think my father ever despaired, not even when he was taken away to the concentration camp at Dachau before his disappearance and no trace afterwards, as it happened to so many. That was how I lost him. Even there in Dachau I am sure whatever his sufferings, his service amongst his brothers and sisters in affliction was to give love and laughter.

'That is why persons love clowns so much. And how true is the saying about the nature of a clown, that if you give him a finger, he will take your hand! So I will not lay stress upon the misery. In my biography, if ever you write it, I ask you to make of it one short chapter only. The misery was in Berlin, in those bombed-out war years, when one saw so much of the sufferings of others.

'Back to my first memory, the face of my father. My mother died in giving me birth, so he made himself both to me and gave me all his care. Wherever he travelled in other countries following the circus he took me with him.

'At what age do we begin to remember in strong outline, to become cognisant that we are persons, each one of us, a small world within ourselves?

'From five years old it was so with me, the happy years when I was the darling-child, the circus-baby with legs so short I could not mount three high caravan steps, only crawl up and toddle all round the big tent in the grass when it was being put up and before it was open for the crowds to come in. Oh, how I loved to sniff up the smell of the damp grass after it had been trodden and stamped upon! It is the smell of the breath of Mother Earth, and a little new-born infant has the same lovely smell as the fragrant grass. I cannot convey it to you, but press your nose close to the earth and the grass and you will know, and it may move you to write one of your poems.

'And the smell of the circus inside the tent after the performance is over. . . . I can smell that as well, now, to this day. Sawdust and the odour of the horse-droppings that have to be swept up, and the acrid odour of the orange-peel that has been thrown about between the seats by the crowd.

'It is a sweet but so pungent smell as it comes back to me, though I have never visited a circus since the days of my father because I could not bear to go back. A person should never go back to where one was happy. It is not there any more. It is impossible to recapture. It could not be, not as it was. Do you follow me, my friend? To try to recapture the past is to see ghosts, or if not to see then to feel their presence.'

Gerard nodded in sure assent. He was too impressed to halt the thread of her narrative by extraneous speech or query. He was enthralled as when a small boy, himself filled with circus-fever, the excitement, sounds and scent of the ringside atmosphere had enthralled him.

'And then the animals, those who were not intended by nature to be performers amusing a multitude by the tricks their trainers have taught them, taking the bows and the applause as if they were the clever ones, and not the four-legged noble creatures who still do not appear silly even though at a word of command or some sign or crack of the whip, they must jump through hoops, erect themselves on two legs in a ridiculous, uncomfortable position and waltz or prance to band-music or the sharp crack of the ring-master's long whiplash; the elephants with all their primeval strength and dignity which is their heritage from the ages, or the pride and the royal appearance of the cheetahs, the tigers and lions whose prison for life is their barred cages. What crime have they committed against society that such unjust punishment should be dealt to them? I have the same emotions when I think of the so many Zoological Gardens where free creatures born with two legs – men, women, and children – may walk around freely or stand and stare.

'When so small, at five years old, my dear papa would lead me by the hand around their cages. One tiger, his name was Rajah, who had once attacked his trainer, but not badly enough to kill him, was my special friend to whom I gave my love and pity, for I had heard it said that though valuable and worth much money to his trainer, he would be shot if he bared his teeth and showed his temper again.

'So I went to his cage and whispered and pleaded with him to be a good tiger. I put my hand between the bars and stroked his beautiful yellow and black striped coat, and he rolled over, pushing out his paw as if to shake hands and promise me he would be a good tiger.

'After that, while he remained with the circus, every evening before bed-time Rajah would give me his paw and make a rattle in his throat.

'Dear Rajah! I can see him now, though he is no longer caged. In his spirit he must be free again and roaming in the jungle where he was first captured and caught to be put in prison behind bars and trained. When the war was on and there were no more circuses, I have no doubt he was dispatched like so many other wild beasts who could not be maintained because meat food must be apportioned and rationed, otherwise there would not be enough for humans.

'War. How old was I at that time? I was seventeen years old when it came to a conclusion, a waif living for many years amongst the stones and rubble and ruin that had changed Berlin from a proud and noble city to a waste land of desolation and destruction. It was in 1937 that my papa was seized by the Nazis in their fearful purge which oppressed all who had the smallest quantity of Jewish blood in their veins, and from Berlin he was conveyed to the concentration camp in Dachau.

'While he was in Dachau I received two letters only, smuggled out to me, and after that – nothing. This is something that has happened twice in my life, to know nothing and to have to accept that nothing will ever be known.

21

'Inquiries were made by someone who was interested in me and anxious to dispel my anxiety, but no information was ever obtainable. My papa was no longer there.

'It is my only consolation, and I cling to it and I will continue to think and believe that, like Rajah the tiger, in his spirit state he is free also and in that glorious condition can continue to travel and to hear the laughter of happy, delighted children.'

4

'WHAT was it like for a homeless little one in a besieged city in those years of affliction and catastrophe, seeking what little safety there was underground in shelters, dug-outs, or the cellars of ruined dwellings? What sort of life was it? How forcibly it comes back to me and refuses to be obliterated!

'A life of noises made by gun-fire and bombing, the whining of shells, the wailing of sirens and the moans of the miserable, the weeping of women whose hearts have been torn and broken, the wretchedness that comes out of a nation's upheaval because a madman had dreamt an ideological dream that in waking he might have imagined might come true without destruction, demolition, savagement by fire and sword and all evil let loose.

'I do not think in the beginning that Hitler was altogether mad. He had the ideas and there was art within him. He wished to paint. At one time he must have perceived beauty in the colours of the sky and in the dawns and the sunsets, in the moonshine when it sets a path of silver and gold upon the sea like a staircase leading to the stars.

'His undoing was the power invested in him by the place-seekers, the greedy ones who made of him what would bring aggrandizement to themselves, treasures and riches. They had perceived that his passionate harangues and shoutings in the public places were preparing the great bonfire, the conflagration that would give them all that they wanted. So his mind was split and the dreamer changed into the schizophrenic.

'Amongst the leaders of men of all races and colour how many, if they were not in places of power, would not be receiving treatment for the mentally deranged?

'When I was growing up into a thin, teen-age girl in those fearful days amidst the stones and rubbish-heaps of what had been imposing buildings and once comfortable homes, some large, some small, an old gentleman who was a great thinker known for his explorations into the intricate workings of the mind would talk to me and lend me the books that he had written. I could not understand them all. They were far beyond my intellect at that time, but much that I was unable to grasp he would explain to me. He had more pity for Hitler than blame. To understand all kinds of things is to be able to forgive so much, to love and to forgive. He had such complete friendship for all humanity. His was a most beautiful character. Like my papa, he never thought about himself.

'How fast I talk on! Deter me, if you wish to, please. My stockpot of recollections of when I was a child and, later on, a young girl made older than my years, is on the boil like the stockpot for soup every Continental knows how to make with all the scraps and pieces thrown in, and the embers of those fires beneath have been stirred so that the lid is lifted up. I apologize. I am not an egotist. There is a question you would like to ask? What is it?'

'There is a gap here of some years after your father was torn from you and you were still a child. Who looked after you and cared for you?'

'There were many so kind persons. Where there is much trouble and misfortune there is always much kindness. In so many the worst brings out the best,

24

'The person who first took me under her protection and provided for me in the best way she could had been an actress in her younger days, very experienced and with art in her finger-tips. What you call in English a straight actress, dramatic, serious, and she had played a diversity of great rôles, but now she was old with a figure amplified, and the meagre diet on which we were all forced to live did not reduce her to slimness. What an artist! An exponent of mime and movement, the richness of her speaking voice was without quaver of age! She took me to live with her in what had been the basement kitchen of a broken home, so we had a stove that someone mended for us, and two twisted bedsteads to sleep in. In such a way, everyone contrived somehow that there should be amenities of a kind. To a child that did not seem so bad at all. She gave me warmth and love and cherishment.

'My greatest amusement was a large wicker basket that she had been able to preserve – the theatrical hamper that she had always travelled with containing her stage dresses, imitation flowers and beads, scarves and pieces of silk. What treasure trove for a juvenile miss in which to be allowed to delve! When she was teaching me to act she would dress me up in a long skirt with a train to it that I must manage to kick backward out of the way so as to move gracefully without too much haste. When she was particularly pleased with my progress, to encourage me and give me the sensitive feeling for an audience that must be the test for an artist, she would invite friends of our peculiar world whose necessities had caused us all to live like the rabbits burrowing underground, to come and see me, and any others who had a talent to sing or to play an instrument would contribute to the entertainment. Oh, yes, we had our moments of fun.

'In addition to the dramatic studies there was another

25

expression of the arts to which I was introduced and which I increasingly adored. To be a ballet dancer was my fierce ambition. As it so happened, the world-famous former *ballerina assoluta*, Ada Karvoska, was in our midst, and she was another one who so beneficently took interest in training me to stand up on my points, to pirouette and spin myself, to leap and bound and skim around, and to feel myself that glorious sensation of being more of the air than of the ground.

'To be a ballet performer was what I had set my heart upon, where all the sensibilities are expressed in the poetry of motion and mime, the warmth, the glow, the verve, rapture, ecstasy and ravishment set to music.

'My friend, perhaps you are not a *balletomane* in its fullest meaning, one who is impelled to follow its dedicated exponents in their interpretations of all the fluctuations of existence?'

Gerard replied:

'Although very much of a layman, the ballet to me is on a height with the finest music transmitted by the most inspired musicians which interprets the choreography of the universe.'

Frieda gave a satisfied nod.

'I am glad. We will visit a performance together at Covent Garden to see Fonteyn one evening, if you care to? The management always places a box at my disposal and I am a personal friend of that great artist. She understands why I like to sit back, hidden by the curtains, because sometimes I have to shed some tears and I am not aware they stream in rivers down my cheeks after my eyes have overflowed. Why should this be so? It is not painful to behold their wonderful movements. It is an exquisite ecstasy which carries me away. . . .'

The telephone bell on her writing desk started to ring: 'Oh, who can this be? I told them at the reception counter I was not to be available unless it happened to be a call from my agent.' She picked up the receiver and replaced it when she had received her answer. 'It is from Mr. Al Parker. Urgent. He wishes to see me immediately at his Park Lane offices. I must go. I cannot refuse such an important man as Mr. Al Parker for the good reason – do not be surprised – that I have to make money. I have not much money except what I earn. I lost most of it. I have given, because I refuse to lend. To wish to be paid back is a meanness, so I do not grieve or grumble over that. I was able to help some persons and make them very happy. I have always been glad to give rather than to withhold, and not to count or question. Please excuse me now that I am not able to remain. Let me write in my date book the time when you will call again, though I am not likely to forget it or make a cancellation. There are certain dates that remain so with a ring round them in the mind. *Auf wiedersehen*, my friend.'

5

ON his way to see Frieda at the time she had fixed a few afternoons later Gerard, who was too fastidious for dalliance with women, found himself halting outside a flower-shop. Those bunches of lilac in her lounge should be ready to be replaced by fresh ones it occurred to him and, as he had sensed rightly that lilac was one of her favourite blossoms, and as it was the season when lilac was in flower, there was a display of these blooms in the window beside carnations, camellias, orchids and other exotic flowers.

Today, as so often happened in the month of May, there was a nip of chill in the air, and according to the weather reports there had been a sprinkling of snow in the higher parts of the Midlands, heavy falls in Scotland and Northern England caused by Icelandic air-currents.

In London snow-clouds loomed heavily, mingling with the fog and petrol fumes. Just one of those days when the smiling face of Nature was obscured and depressions clamped down upon individuals as well as the weather. There could be no hint of sunshine to break through today. Gerard wondered if the gloomy conditions had depressed Frieda. Anyhow, it must be the lilac blooms for her. He went in and bought an ornamental basketful just as he saw it arranged in the shop window, with a huge bow of pale mauve satin ribbon tied on the handle.

What an interesting-looking man, thought the girl

attendant who had an elaborate bird's nest hair-do, and a sheath-like frock which proclaimed her vital statistics. Her assiduous dancing of the Twist made slimming pills unnecessary. What sort of woman, she wondered, could he be in love with? Most likely he had a dull, uninteresting wife he never bought flowers for, and this was just one of those affairs on the side. She served so many of that kind, but he didn't look like it somehow. That was just what made him so interesting – the shaggy black-and-grey-sprinkled hair, the craggy features and penetrating, dark, deep-set eyes, all contributing to evoke a certain romantic appeal in one like herself with no time or inclination for reading, but who was not essentially different from those of an age before her who had. The only difference in her era was that you knew it all. You knew too much, if anything. You found out for yourself too soon and nobody ever told you.

Besides flower sales-girl by occupation, she was a dance-hall exponent of the 'Twist' and had won a prize recently of twenty-five pounds. Not that twenty-five pounds meant much in these days. She made a pretty little grimace. Still, it had enabled her to buy herself an evening frock she would be wearing next time. She was already entered for another competition, and if she could last out for the fifty pounds attempt she would treat herself to a nylon coat that you couldn't tell was not real leopard-skin. All the while she was doing up Gerard's purchase in tissue paper her hips were swaying in movement that had become almost a habit. 'Besides, I do it for practice as well, y'know,' so she informed him. 'It's the thing to do to keep in practice, whatever it is, especially dancing.'

'And do you call the "Twist" dancing?' Gerard put it to her. He had been drawing her out to talk all the time, even to telling him her age, which was eighteen.

'Well, you know, it's what the savages do, isn't it, and if it's dancing to them, why shouldn't it be dancing for us?' She gave him the apt-enough excuse for the latest ballroom craze. 'You do ask questions, don't you?'

'Well, it happens to be my job, and so it also becomes a habit,' Gerard explained.

'Asking questions! Do you get paid for that?'

'Certainly. I'm a journalist.'

'A journalist? That means you write!'

'After I've asked enough questions, yes. It's how I do it.'

'Mind if I ask you one then?' The girl stuck in the last tiny pin keeping the tissue paper folds in place.

'Ask away!'

'Who are these flowers for? Thirty-five shillings, please, with the basket. It's the basket that costs the most. You needn't have bought the basket as well if you didn't want it; I could have taken the flowers out.'

'I thought they looked just right in the basket, all ready arranged and filled with soft moss at the roots to keep them fresh.'

'I did the arranging. I like arranging flowers, y'know. I like touching them.'

'You did it very well. Most artistic. I am taking these to a famous lady, an actress from America who is in London at the moment to appear in a musical imported from Broadway in which she was the star.'

'Are you in love with her, or is love the wrong word for it?'

'I admire her very much. I think she is a very talented, wonderful person.'

'Do you go to see her very often?'

'This is the second time only, but I hope to see her fairly frequently before she leaves again.'

'Ow!' She had the genuine Cockney's intonation made so familiar in television plays. 'Are you taking her the flowers to make her talk some more?'

'Not for that reason at all. Those particular flowers are her favourite, and seeing them in the window I wanted to buy them for her.'

'Have you a wife at home?'

'No wife. Why do you ask?'

'Then that's all right. 'Cos if you had, I don't think it is right, y'know, getting mixed up with someone else and causing a lot of trouble perhaps.'

'I'm surprised to hear you say that!'

'Why?'

'Because nowadays youngsters like yourself are not often credited with thinking in that considerate way.'

'Lots of people don't understand us boys and girls. We don't dress the same and we don't talk the same, I suppose, so everybody thinks we're as wild as we seem to them, but we're not, not really. It's partly the fault of the Bishops who say what awful kids we are. There was a Bishop who talked to Adam Faith once on television about religion, and I looked in that night because I wanted to hear what Adam Faith thought, not what the Bishop thought, but this Bishop he might have been one of us. He talked like a man, not a holy Joe. Your change – seven-and-six.' She proffered the coins.

'Buy yourself some violets instead, or whatever you fancy to pin into your jacket.'

'Thanks. S'nice of you. When a girl works in a flower-shop nobody ever thinks of giving her flowers. You're a gentleman who calls himself a journalist. I do look at a newspaper sometimes for the telly programmes to see what's on, or what's happening to Liz Taylor or any of the names that work like a slot-machine for bringing in the cash. Shouldn't think they get much out of it to last in the long run. Flowers fade and stars drop out of the sky. What newspaper do you work for? I'll look out for your stuff if you'll tell me your name. That's if it prints your name.'

'It does. Gerard Hemming representing the *Daily Flight*.'

'Then I know you!' She made the discovery. 'Of course I couldn't tumble to it before, because you never turn your face to the viewers on the telly.' She handed him the wrapped-up flower-basket. 'And you won't think me rude, will you, if I pass the remark, but I should ask the producer to have your face turned round for people to see. It's a nice enough face, you know. Pleased to meet you.'

6

FRIEDA was awaiting him in the lounge of her private suite when Gerard arrived. She had been sitting on a low stool beside the electric fire with its semblance of glowing logs which she had switched on to give warmth to this inhospitable day. He noticed the extremely simple suit she was wearing. It was of some pale mauve soft material with a silk scarf of a pearly shade tinted with little splashes of sea-green which matched her eyes, and a necklace made up of several rows of small iridescent, tropical sea-shells that mingled the green and blue of the sea. She had evidently been feeling chilly because she had a green car-rug wound around her lower limbs and tucked in tightly at her feet which gave her the aspect of a mer-nymph – a hybrid of the ocean.

As the hotel attendant announced his name she cast aside the rug from her feet with a single gesture and a glad exclamation of welcome and came forward at a little run to greet him; then suddenly she almost seemed to trip as if some former injury to one of her tiny feet had recurred and halted her quick-stepping, but he was beside her and, catching hold of his arm, she steadied herself and held to it for a moment.

'Pardon. That was a clumsy approach.' The brightness of her smile was like a blink of sunshine that atoned for the murk and coldness outside. 'My Queen Alexandra limp!

When there is snow or rain to come it asserts itself and in my ankle and instep – the left one – the peculiar ache is a barometer, a weather portent which never fails. Come and refresh yourself at the tea-table. I thought you would be punctual, so I had it in readiness. If you are punctual for the B.B.C. you would be the same for me, but you must not let me become tedious at any time. When you interview your celebrity guinea-pigs I have observed that you are so skilful in your dissection after you have opened them up that it makes a person agreeable to be under your interrogation. To like to be interviewed for the millions is a little puzzling to me.'

'It isn't really. Amongst certain individuals it may be conceit and big-headedness, but one doesn't select those if one can avoid it. In the main, my celebrity visitors I look upon in the spirit in which they come and consent to be there, like the blood-donors who give because they feel it is needed.'

'Then I am different. You think it was selfish of me to withhold my life story? To tell it to you in camera, not before the cameras, it is an indulgence that refreshes me to open these press-studs over my lips.'

'I don't look upon it, in that way. You are giving something in another form that will be as self-revealing, though you will not appear before the public on the films or the stage or on television, but on the printed page which will be read by many in this autobiography you are telling me.'

'Autobiography as I am speaking it, but biography if later in your judgment you consider it to be important enough to be found inside the covers of a book,' she reminded him, 'otherwise I could not unseam myself. As it is, I am feeling there is such a flow of sympathy between us, like two trains which are proceeding towards some halting station on parallel lines, and there is nothing I shall be too reluctant to hold back. Oh, but how considerate and kind of you! Those beautiful lilacs for me!' Gerard had been removing the tissue paper wrappings from the flower-basket he had brought with him, and now, diffidently, he held it up for her to see.

'Where would you like me to put them?'

'Oh, thank you! Here, close by me on the table beside the tea-tray. The ones in my inner room were faint and drooping, finished with their flower existence. This morning I told the chambermaid to remove them, so later on that is where I shall take them to my bed-table with Nemo's, my illustrious papa's photograph beside them, for he also had a fondness for the lilacs of Austria, the country he loved to travel in best of all in the circus journeyings when I was so small. As happy as the day is long would be the description of what it was like when I was five years old and the first transfer pictures in the brightest colours were becoming fast pasted into my mind for always. Memory is the treasurer and guardian of all things, and I am thankful that in my storehouse I have so much richness that only old age, the thief of time, can steal.

'The lilacs of Austria and of that little postage-stamp size principality of Lichtenstein adjoining – how the sight and the smell of them stir me as if I had returned again to the happiness I can still savour in such tender memories preserved by love!

'Austria! That ravishing country of so much enchantment, full of the sparkle of living in those halcyon days of Arcadia, when the heavenly kingdom appeared to be on earth and everyone rejoiced. Austria with its deeply-wooded forests of sweet-smelling pine trees and larch, where I have seen fairies peeping behind the pines and little men in

35

green. They were quite real to me. As children we see these unsubstantial beings until the heavy veil that is called realism is suddenly dropped like a steel curtain that cannot be raised again.

'To re-vision it again, as I am doing now, is making me feel like a painter who, after a long period because his fingers have been crushed, is given a brush to use once more.

'I can see them now – those wooden châlets perched upon the hillsides, the proud schlosses made of colossal blocks of stone which look as if they had been quarried and hewn by Titans, where the barons lived and hunted and rode, the care-free peasantry in their pretty, colourful costumes, always so smiling and gay, and the old peasant women with the creased faces like the ripened apples in their own orchards, all smiles, smiles all the while!

'Our biggest circus dates would be in Austria, commencing with Vienna, Salzburg and many other towns. My papa was honoured to appear before Dr. Dolfuss, the great Chancellor who was assassinated by the Nazis.

'Oh, the panorama of those scenes unfolding so fast before me! The gleeful merriment of laughter and folk-dancing in the open places, where the tables would be set out in the sunshine under the brightly coloured garden umbrellas and awnings; the beersteins of lager being refilled and topped with froth as soon as drunk; and stringed instruments, the violin especially, pouring out such sweet sounds of gypsy music and the waltzes of Strauss, the greatest composer of his time. And I can see in mind-pictures the wayside shrines made of wood or stones with the little bunches of flower offerings placed before the holy statuettes by the devout, and at sunset I can hear the ringing of the Angelus bells when even the farm-labourer pauses to pray and to say his Ave Marias. Prayers, for the simplest people of all the

36

nations, are as the key of the day and the lock of the night.

'I have never re-visited Austria since I was that innocent child when happiness and tranquillity came to an end in Berlin. That was after I was six years old, the circus was folded up, and the persecution and the purges were the prelude to the wicked warfare which made me an orphan, growing-up amidst the conditions in Berlin of which I have told you, and the youth of nations was summoned to fight for those who chose to declare war. Always it is youth who must go forth before there has been time for the sweets of life to be tasted. War loves to seek its victims in the young.

'This now brings me to the accident that happened to me when the greatest disappointment of my life brought an end to my aspiration to become a ballerina, and I was flown back to England with five broken ribs that were still bound up, and a smashed instep with all the little snapped bones in it encased in tight plaster for six whole months. Please pass your cup. Let me fill it up again, and I will tell you the rest.'

7

'TAKE a glance for yourself at my foot which was injured. Look!' Frieda removed the low-heeled shoe that was $2\frac{1}{2}$ in English size, and stretched out the dainty foot in its filmy nylon stocking of texture so fine that the pretty toes could be seen through it, for Gerard's inspection. She wriggled them up and down, and stiffened and relaxed the ankle backwards and forwards and circular-wise so that it did not appear to him, who could only admire and marvel at its shapeliness, that she had been so handicapped. Those assiduously practised movements had all been taught to her by the physiotherapists and she had persevered with them patiently, strong in her resolve that she must be able to dance again.

Unaccustomed to express himself in any gesture that was un-English, he felt the impulse nevertheless to bend forward and press his lips courtier-wise over the highly-arched instep, but refrained, nevertheless, and said instead:

'It looks a most perfect little foot to me.'

She inserted it into the shoe again.

'In restoring its shape the surgeons made a very good job of it. Excellent. The bones in the ankle and the instep are so many and so complicated that a very bad crush such as mine can make a complete repair impossible, but to have been enabled through all their skill to walk easily, and very seldom to show any signs of the disability, is something to be thankful for. I can still remain an actress in comedy or drama, but never the dancer I desired to be, to leap and bound and pirouette in ballet. It was my tragedy, but life is full of compensations, and the poise, the equilibrium and the balance is restored in other ways, of which the first and hardest lesson was not to accept defeat. The bones of the body may be broken, but the spirit is not to be shattered unless one is a weak and ineffectual person without the determination to win through. "Guts" is the word. Guts that will enable a climber to scale the highest peak of a mountain or a man to orbit the earth in a capsule through space.

'What a great privilege it is to appreciate the gift of existence and of life, whether it is bestowed in the form of a flower that withers only to bloom again in another season, or a bird, or to be a man or woman. To me it is quite apparent that all of it for each one of us is planned and ordained and of an exact pattern, from the colourings upon a butterfly's wings to the ornamental markings of a snake's skin, the spots of a leopard, the stripes of a tiger. The powerful Designer of all has arranged the smallest detail, including the décor and the decorations, but if we attempt to rebel or to think we could make our own design for ourselves we only discover our mistake too late. He could not be expected to put back the whole universe for one person, for that would be to overthrow the universe itself.

'My so-kind, learned old friend, the philosopher, who was in refuge with us in those times of distress when we were in hiding in Berlin, explained so many things that he had written in his books which came back to me when I was puzzled, rebellious and impatient. He died shortly before my accident in a most peaceful manner, sitting in his chair. I shall never forget his benevolent countenance, with

39

the white moustache and beard shining like a nimbus around the head of a saint. Perhaps he was a saint, for I believe there are saints sent to live upon this earth to help and strengthen, just as there are heavenly messengers and protectors in our midst who do not appear in shining garments with wings, so that we are not aware of their visitations until they have departed on their heavenly errands. Often when I was lying in hospital in great agony, unable to move, it would be more comfort to me to recall his teachings than to press the bell for the night-nurse to ask for help to ease my position.

'It is a peculiar thing that on occasions I can perceive faces of those who were so dear to me and still near though no longer here. It is not my thoughts or my imaginings that conjure them, or the approach of the dream state before the white moss of slumber falls over my lids. I am fully awake although I have closed my eyes. They are there of themselves. They are not ghosts. Ghosts are but pale reflections of restless persons who have left their unhappy vibrations behind. It is so satisfying to see these loved faces form and to have the assurance that parting through death brings no division. There is a bridge flung between, over which they may walk, and love is the principle on which it is constructed of a material that is so delicate that it is invisible but indestructible because love can never die.

'I have seen the clown's face of my papa as he always ran straight out of the circus immediately after the last performance to bend over my pillow and murmur "*Guten nacht, liebschen*" before he retired to remove his grease-paint, his false forehead and bald pate and divest himself of his striped pantaloons in his own partition of our caravan.

'I talk on and on! Why do you not break it skilfully with a question as you do in your television interviews when you wish to bring your sitter back to the subject if he or she has strayed from it?

'So I am back to the accident which took place in a second when the balancing hand of my partner, the strong man who was holding me aloft over his head poised upon his palm, loosed its hold because his foot had stumbled and I was precipitated into a sprawl which sent me into a far corner exactly as a piece of china would be smashed if thrown so hard against a wall.

'The war was just over, but you understand what it was like while it was still raging, and afterwards when peace had been proclaimed. On the announcement of peace and cessation from killing it was not easy to see the sky full of white doves on the instant. Life still has to go on, but misery in the destroyed cities remained unspeakable. What was happening to you in those days? I ask so little, but if there was time I would like you to tell me of all that has befallen you as well.'

'During part of the war I was over Germany in the R.A.F. I know what Berlin was like – as in London, the black harvest following upon destruction.'

'And amongst it all the bright lights of night clubs and entertainments, the flaunting of riches, the dissipations, the grossness and libertinism, but amidst it all there were those white angels who were keeping watch.

'In Berlin now to earn what I could for myself and also because it was a good chance to keep up the practice that might eventually bring me into the world of ballet, I obtained employment in a small cabaret where I danced, and the proprietor engaged also to act as my partner, a big hefty young German who had come out of the Army. He had been a wrestler, and also in acrobatic dancing he had some previous experience as what is called a supporter.

There was no harm in him. He had a pleasant nature. His weakness was that he had a tendency to become drunk; then I would lack confidence in case he would be unable to maintain the steady balance without the slightest movement when the poise of my body was dependent only upon him.

'I had spoken of this fear to a new friend I had met with, who had come in recently as a spectator with a few other companions who were Americans like himself, and they had invited me to their table for refreshment afterwards. Apple-juice is my drink; never anything else. Intoxicants do not agree with me, and I cannot even bear the smell of men who overdrink when they come near to me since that night when I could tell by the smell of my partner's sweat as soon as we were in close proximity, that he was in a bad condition. The smell of beer given off by the flesh of an overheated man is most unpleasant and it made me feel sick.

'In the involuntary effort he made to control the stagger that unplaced his foot, his hold of me relaxed and I had no support. I could do nothing. If I had been a trapeze performer suspended by an insecure strap and without a safety net to fall into, the result would have been as disastrous. The damage was done. I was not unconscious. One moment the pianist and violinist who accompanied us had been playing the exquisite composition, *Liebstraum*, and the next the music was cut off and I was being carried away limp and helpless into the dressing-room by the young American officer and his companions. They laid me on the floor very concernedly. My dancing partner was kneeling beside me, sobbing and entreating me to try to stand up.

'I tried to smile and assure him his careless slip had not injured me too seriously, and I would have attempted to stir if I could, but my body stayed motionless.

'Agony began shooting through my ribs and my foot. I heard the sharpness of my own agonized screams which I could not stop as the pains stabbed through me like long knives in my side and shorter knives amputating my foot. I heard the musicians in the cabaret strike up again and a negro-woman singing as loudly as a Siamese cat in season. All was consternation, exactly like one of those fatalistic scenes on television.

'The young American who had carried me in placed his hand with gentle authority upon my shoulder and said in in such a quiet voice:

' "Don't move! Keep still. I'm a doctor, and the first thing to be done is to find out right now what your injuries are."

'Then he proceeded to make his careful examination by which his first diagnosis was afterwards confirmed by the X-rays, which was that I had sustained five broken ribs, a broken instep and a broken ankle.'

8

Frieda's low musical voice ceased. Gerard did not prompt her. He waited until, of her own accord, she was ready to continue.

She was leaning back in the capacious armchair with her eyes closed as if to shut out the agonizing recollection. How fragile she looked, how small and exquisitely formed, as delicate as a vase shaped in the poetic contours of a woman, a vessel which might well have held the wine of genius as a queen of the ballet. Although she had made the most out of the second-best in her career as a stage and film actress and succeeded so brilliantly almost beyond dreams he could feel deeply moved by, and share, her pangs and regrets for the highest creative instincts within her as an artist which had proved unfulfilled and unattainable after the vase had been shattered, although so skilfully repaired as to appear undiscernable.

She was aware of his sympathy and understanding flowing towards her. Pity was the least consolation. Pity had not helped her at any time, not even when she had been first hurt and so afflicted that the expression of pity increased her sensibility and suffering instead of helping to soften or allay it. His silence told her more than words that he was walking beside her in thought every step of the painful way.

Tears crept between her eyelids and they opened. With her fingers she pushed the drops back again.

Still not speaking, she reached for the handbag beside her chair and taking from it a pocket mirror, she held it up with one hand before her face as she proceeded to perform an interesting little ritual which had nothing to do with the dusting-over of powder from a compact or any form of beauty aid.

Mystified, he watched her. She was pushing and holding up her lips at the corners with her forefinger, from one side of her mouth to the other. They had been quivering, down-drooping. She continued the operation several times, smiling into the mirror; then replaced it in her handbag and looked directly at Gerard. The smile, like all else she performed, was an achievement.

'I am out of my pocket of silence. *Danksein*,' she said in gratitude for his consideration. 'I still think in the German language first before I speak, and so the polite words come out sometimes. Do you wish me to resume?'

'Very much indeed. Unless you would rather not.'

'I prefer. It is a relief like a released limb from the tight plaster of Paris as they break it up to take off in little pieces with the large pair of surgical scissors. Six months I was in that case of discomfort from my instep to my thigh, and after it was removed there had to be another shorter plaster from the ankle to below the knee for another two months. Tight bandages also for my five broken ribs. So is it any wonder that I have been a repressed person and con-strained as well in my speech? Miss Iceberg was one of the names that has been given to me by those who had thought it might be an amusement to de-freeze me. I was not amused. The news-hounds made so much publicity out of my seeming indifference. Excuse those words. I do not place you in such hunting company which has some of the character of the blood-sports I am opposed to. There are

45

the exceptions who are knights of the pen and so I regard you.'

'Thank you,' said Gerard. 'That is more than sufficient accolade for me. Do you mind if I ask you a question? When you took your mirror from your handbag just now and pushed up your lips. What did it mean? What made you do that?'

'I will tell you. When I was in hospital after those weeks and weeks of pain I did not know how to smile again. I was so miserable, but one morning after the washing of me was finished and the nurse had been brushing and combing my hair, she took out of my locker a small circular *toilette* mirror and put it into my hand lying over the coverlet.

' "This is not mine," I said. I had been conveyed to the hospital without anything personal, and all necessities, even to the nightgowns I had been wearing, were provided from the hospital store for emergency patients. In all those many days and weeks of surgical treatment I was scarcely aware of myself being under the drug I had been given to reduce the pain. Like a lifeless rag-doll, my body and my face were attended to and washed, and two nurses would raise me with dexterous movements and substitute fresh linen sheets, sliding them away and under me. For weeks my neck had been tied very tightly into a thick padded collar of cotton wool covered with gauze, because at the back of my neck there had also been detected a small splintering or fracture. It was a very uncomfortable confinement – my horse-collar, the nurse called it when she was fixing it to ease it every day. But at last it was to be taken off and I could roll my neck about on the pillow, and after the morning blanket-bath I was propped up in a sitting position with three pillows supported by a wooden bed-rest. I was in a small private ward to myself, which I was told later was a special

46

privilege. How kind they all were, so cheerful and wonderful all the time, those Red Cross nurses!

'There was the mirror in my hand and the nurse told me why she had put it there.

' "I brought it for you," she said. "Wouldn't you like to take a look at yourself, honey, now that you can sit up at last? It might cheer you up to see your own face. You might have broken your nose and your jaw, but your face escaped; not a single bruise. You are just as pretty as you ever were. You should be thankful. Your face might have been smashed like a china doll's, and then even if it was repaired by plastic surgery you would not have been able to smile. Now, look!"

'Still I was not interested, so she took the mirror from me and held it up before my face. It was the same face. The pain and agonies of the days and nights had been so excruciating I would have expected to see the face of a very aged person, but pain had not written any signature upon my face.

'Physical pain, I have noticed, is very merciful in that way. It is the anguish of mental suffering, sorrow and overmuch worry that is like the burrowing woodworm which causes such ravagement in the human features and bleaches the hair. My face was still young and my hair as red as before.'

'Chestnut.' Gerard corrected her description of the deeply rich shade that Nature had set and waved without any of the devices of the most expert hairdresser. Her hair grew high up, brushed back from her forehead and confined by a narrow tortoiseshell band.

'I gazed into the mirror at my own woeful face, so young and so depressed. I was not relieved, for all my thoughts when not centred upon the agony I had been

47

enduring were of the ballet and if I would be able to take up my studies and how soon, once I could find my way into some school of advanced instruction. I listened to what the nurse was telling me as one who was giving me the right prescription that I must follow on with and continue:

' "You are pretty, honey," she was saying, "but it is not fair to yourself or other people you will meet to have those drooping lips always. To smile and to appear happy is to make other people happy. It is what every woman should be able to do, or make herself do even if she doesn't feel like smiling. A woman without a smiling face is not fulfilling her mission in life, which is to make others who may be downcast feel cheered up. I don't mean a false put-on tooth-paste smile. Do this – so!" She pushed up the corners of my lips with her finger-tips. "Now, honey, smile! Smile into the mirror. Any time when your lips are turned down, smile into the mirror and you will smile again!" '

9

Now Frieda was smiling across the tea-table at Gerard, not coquettishly, but so sweetly. There was a radiance in her smile, in her rich yet simple and naïve personality, which made her appear amazingly attractive whatever her age might be. The harsh experiences and vicissitudes out of which she had emerged so victorious and essentially unchanged showed her to be a gallant challenger against misfortune who, although she had beaten the clock and won the jackpot of success, still remained her integral self.

His thoughts were a man's thoughts when he contemplated a woman he greatly admires, but in an enhanced degree because he was not only touched by, but appreciative of, her trust and confidence in him.

In the course of his own highly successful journalistic career as a feature-writer, columnist and interviewer, which his television reputation had greatly enhanced, he had encountered a great number of celebrities of all kinds, both male and female; and his experiences in the main of personalities so deftly self-revealed by his direct questioning, had tinged his opinion of the entertainment-world in particular with a certain degree of cynicism, which his own background and lack of home-life and affection had added to when both his celebrated parents had been so centred upon their own careers.

'You are contemplative. Of what are you thinking?' asked Frieda.

'Of you, as you appear to me both as a beautiful woman and an acknowledged artist. You are so utterly unspoilt. Of the Success Women I have met personally, the ones who have remained unspoilt I can count on my ten fingers. There must be others, of course, but the outstanding names that come into my mind are as few as that. In films, theatre and show business, Ingrid Bergman, Flora Robson, Sybil Thorndike, Gracie Fields, Eartha Kitt, Callas the opera singer, Fonteyn, two other contemporary Russian ballerinas and – yourself.'

'*Danksein*.' She acknowledged his tribute. 'A performer who has the mumps above the ears cannot continue to be a true artist. Her integrity is lost, so she becomes top-heavy and her poise is upset. If she is a ballerina her dancing would not remain of the first quality to keep her on a pinnacle balanced on the point of one shoe. Do you wish me to continue?'

'That is why I am here.'

'I have never wished to talk and tell so much before. As a rule I am a silent person, except sometimes, not very often, when I explode. I become a volcano when I am aware my producer is too much thinking of the box-office and not of what I am there to portray. Then I am bound to argue if I am convinced I am right, and there have been some big rows. I must not wander away in my recital except when I have to tell you of the people I can't forget because I never want to forget. They were so dear to me. First then, from the time of my accident, there is the one who succoured and delivered me – my Bill, the American Lieutenant of the United States Army Medical Corps. I have no photograph of him, so I will make one for you. He comes up before me as if he had never died. As if I was beholding him on a television long distance view and hearing his voice from outside the sphere of this earth.

'William Corbett was his name. When the Americans came into the holocaust he had just graduated from Los Angeles Medical University, and was as dedicated to his profession of healing and medical research as the astronaut to his space-travel and the fringe of discoveries upon which he stands in his space suit ready for the moment he is to enter his capsule and to become of a weightlessness which is akin to the ethereal nature of the spirits who are able to travel through space with the swiftness of thought. Space-travel and what will be found out will establish the world of the spirit as well as other worlds. That is my own feeling.

'On the evening Bill first came into the café with his two American Air Force companions, he invited me to their table when I was beside them to enquire their orders, to act as hostess as well as cabaret dancer being a part of my duties. I noticed that he was wearing a narrow white band around his coat sleeve, but I did not know it denoted he was a doctor as he did not speak of himself, not once. The talk between us was light-hearted and gay. He and his friends had chosen to visit our small café in a side-street because the senseless sight of so much destruction and demolition was dreadful to walk amongst and to view, and the contrast between that and the flashy night-spots where strip-teasing was the only entertainment and vice prevailed, was not for them a pleasurable interlude away from their duties. This one was small and well-conducted and the proprietor, who played the violin to the piano accompanist, had been a salaried artist himself before disaster overtook him with the rest of us. He kept a fatherly eye upon the hostesses he employed and was very strict how they conducted themselves.

'My portrait of Bill. Try to see him as I would show you. He was so fine and very tall with fair hair and blue eyes and such clear vision in them, and a complexion that looked like wine flowing and glowing beneath his skin. Anyone would single him out at once amongst a crowd for his height, his erectness and his appearance of abounding physical as well as mental health.

'He showed immediate interest in me without the condescension and familiarity which made me sometimes shrink away from that desire-light which every girl knows is the warning signal for her when it is switched on in a man's eyes. The honesty in his eyes was an assurance; as if someone was beside me who was ready to take my arm to hasten me into safety when the moment came to make the traffic crossing. It is a strange thing. Although I have no fear of an audience once I have got myself over, I am terrified of traffic.

'So I found myself telling him of my happy childhood with the circus and of Nemo, my papa, whose famous name was known to him already, the hatred of Hitler for all with one small tinge of Jewish ancestry which made him torture and destroy them. I told him of how I had lived since, a child-vagrant though cared for by strangers who were also in distress and affliction but moved to protect me out of the kindness of their hearts. Can you tell me, I have often asked myself, why in times of their own prosperity so many should be so cruel, so ungenerous, avaricious and grasping?

'I remember Bill's remark at that time. There was a tone in his voice of such concern and sincerity that I could not mistake it.

52

' "You poor kid! Something will have to be done about this."

'I said I was not so unhappy now that the war was over. My hope was that some visitor of artistic prominence, some person who was connected with the ballet, might see me dancing and be convinced there was a future for me if my student-ship could be arranged. It would be arduous, but I would not mind, however hard, so long as I could be dancing upon a stage where someone who was as great as Karsavina, Pavlova or Markova had flitted at some time.

'Bill said to me:

' "I'll help you all I can. I might contrive to get to know someone who knows someone. That's how these sort of things happen sometimes. You dance like a fairy!" And after that, "Fairy" was his name for me. He never called me anything else.

'Three evenings later there came the accident when my partner loosed his hold and I had the catastrophe of that fall. It was through the influence of Bill that I was at once transported to an American hospital where he was a doctor and made himself responsible for me. An American surgeon who was of great note performed the intricate operations which took place one after the other. For a whole night, so they told me, my life had been in peril. Most of the time I was unconscious under the drugs I was given. I was half out of this world.

'One evening when he must have been doing his nightly routine round of the hospital I became conscious that Bill was standing beside me, gazing down at me most intently, and as I looked up into his eyes the blueness of them was like the sky with the sun making it translucent. He bent over me and whispered in so gentle a tone that not even the

53

night sister who was behind him could have heard his words in which there was entreaty, command, and a rediffusion of strength transmitted from him to me:

  ' "Live, Fairy! Live!"

  'And so I did live. I wished to continue, to go on.'

10

A LAST-MINUTE headline topical article due for tomorrow's issue of his newspaper reminded Gerard he would have to get back to Fleet Street within the hour. It was in the portfolio he had brought with him and he had intended to hand it over to the copy-writer on his way, and then had forgotten all about it in his eagerness to be with Frieda.

He apologized as he told her of its urgency.

'Do not say any more. I understand. It is the same for you as for me. We are the servants of the public, but there is no degradation in any job of work that I can see, and there is pride in service where there is diligence and devotion also. So is the lovely Queen of your country a devoted willing servant, dedicated and true. A newspaper man must serve his newspaper and never let it down. The printing presses have to go on and so also must the show. Make haste or the traffic may delay you.'

'You had more to tell me—'

'So much more, but enough for just now. I shall tell you all my not very important history before I go back to America. Though my funny speech has the foreign accent I am a well-Americanised American subject. I like to visit England and all countries. I have travelled so much and so far, but I am most at home in America especially since Mr. Kennedy has been at the White House. I am often invited as a private guest to lunch with them. I am very fond of

Jackie. She is a natural. However important she is today as her husband's partner, she will always continue to be her natural self. My second husband was at the University with Mr. Kennedy and they were good friends, so with two American husbands it is not surprising that I appreciate my adopted country.'

'Two husbands?' He was taken aback, surprised.

'The first one was Bill, the young American doctor who implored me to live, and the second one was Teddie Hamilton, a famous aviator and test pilot. He might have been amongst the ones most likely to alight upon the moon, if he had lived. I am twice a widow, you see. This is all in my history which I shall unfold to you in my unsorted way. It is like looking into my theatrical hamper which is full of so many bits and pieces, and how much more so with my mind which I am unpacking for you as I talk.'

'When may I see you again? It can't be too often for me, but I mustn't intrude on your other engagements all the same.'

'No matter.' Frieda's shoulders hunched in a slight foreignish shrug which dismissed all else as extraneous. 'I am relaxed when I find myself in your company. I like the gentle silence which descends between us whenever a profound memory stirs my heart and swells the obstruction which comes into my throat so that I cannot swallow. Unless my other appointments are of an imperative nature dictated by my agent, I seldom make any. He attends to all that for me. He is very considerate. When he makes a contract for me I know it is a right one and I put my signature to it and it is done. He is all for the artist, but to the money-men who in the parlance of the theatre are known as angels, he will himself name the highest figure for the artist and not concede one inch. How are you fixed for this evening, Gerard?' She had not called him by his Christian name before. 'I am going to Covent Garden tonight on a most special invitation to be present at a first performance in this country of the young Russian dancer with Fonteyn in "La Giselle". If I had no stockings or shoes I would walk there in the snow on my bare feet not to miss it. Do you care to come with me?'

Gerard accepted gladly.

'I shall be free for the rest of the evening from six o'clock onwards. First how about an early dinner quietly together?' he suggested. 'If you've never been to Fleet Street's most famous eating house, "The Cheshire Cheese," I'd like to take you there. You will absorb the atmosphere, I'm sure.'

'Some other evening I would like to very much, but not tonight if you don't mind,' Frieda declined. 'Of course I have heard of the "Cheshire Cheese" where there is sawdust sprinkled on the floor-boards as in the gone-by days and where so many of the Fleet Street persons who were such great figures in their time can never detach themselves altogether. There would be Charles Dickens and so many English names I do not know that I should know. I am not widely enough educated, but you would tell me. Have a good meal yourself before you fetch me or I shall feel unsocial if you do not eat. You have a big frame to keep energized, for you must work very hard. No, please do not persuade me. Tonight on this very particular occasion I do not wish to partake of food until tomorrow morning. Unless it was you who are coming with me I should prefer to witness this great event in ballet alone. I have a feeling inside me already that it will be an experience never to be forgotten, so call for me early and we can slip unnoticed into the box I am honoured to have had reserved for me.'

When Gerard arrived slightly ahead of the time arranged, Frieda was ready waiting for him.

The latest phases of fashion creativeness as evolved by the handful of top designers in Paris and London were outside his province to describe in details or exactitude. He disliked the *outre*, the freakish or the over-emphasized, and appreciated only the beautiful in line or design. Beholding Frieda as she had arrayed herself, he had to stand still and admire the delicate perfection of the picture she made. The evening frock she was wearing was a blend of some diaphanous materials in varying shades, and slung loosely over her shoulders was a short cape of deep purple trimmed with narrow edgings and collar of chinchilla. Her hair, combed straight back from the forehead, clustering in its natural curls around her ears and to the nape of her neck, was confined by a swathed band of mauve satin topped with a big bow, a decoration which she had removed from the handle of the flower-basket filled with lilac he had given her that afternoon. Other women attending the ballet performance at Covent Garden would have their elaborately arranged heads adorned with glittering tiaras, but not one could surpass the simple effectiveness of the satin bow in contrast to the richness of her chestnut hair.

Then he found adequate speech.

'How marvellous you look! Dior, I suppose, or one of those?'

She was pleased.

'You approve my dress? That is good. It is my own idea. I made it myself. I make all my clothes, but most persons imagine by my dress when I go out that I must be an expensive woman because I like to be exclusive to myself. It is so much easier than to adapt oneself to the ideas of a master designer who has first draped his fabrics over one of his models while he improvises and cuts. I travel with my sewing-machine wherever I go, and in a hour or less of my arrival, I have spread my material on the carpet where I kneel to cut it by guess without a pattern, wind it around me, pin it and then sew and it is all finished. It satisfies me and makes me feel as the flower when it is putting out some fresh petals. Have you kept the taxi waiting? I am feeling so *allegro*, elated. The lights are up in my heart.'

'I left my own little Mini-minor just round the corner.'

'Splendid! Then we can arrive and depart without any hindrance.'

They arrived at the Opera House while there were still many seats to be taken up and proceeded straight to the small box for two into which the attendant showed them.

Frieda handed the man a small package she had taken out of her handbag.

'For Madam Fonteyn. My name is written outside with the message to open it before the curtain rises. Please will you see that is it conveyed to her immediately?'

'It was such a small gift inside that I wished her to have as a symbol of my admiration and affection,' Frieda told Gerard when the attendant had withdrawn. 'For all the years since I have been widowed I have kept it in my jewel-case amongst my few valuables, not many. My little gift was the R.A.F. Squadron Leader's wing-badge which was on my flying second husband's sleeve, and so who more suited to possess it than the one who had the white wings of a *ballerina assoluta* to lift her off her feet? She will know what made me give her the wings of my airman.' She looked down from over the ledge of the box. 'How quickly it is filling up! Tonight there will not be one single vacant seat. The orchestra commences to tune itself. Soon we shall be transported into the world of ballet, of mime and movement, joined together in such perfection as if the ones who we shall be looking upon have come to dance for us from some far star. Hold my hand, Gerard, to steady me. I am all trembling.'

He held it tightly as she slid it into his. It felt like a small icicle.

'How cold it is!'

'For the first few moments until the late bell rings and the lights are lowered. Then, to the fingertips, it will be as if I am holding both hands before a glowing brazier and all of me will become ignited, incandescent!'

11

As the heavy stage curtains were slowly raised, Frieda leant forward over the box-ledge.

She had not withdrawn her cold little hand from Gerard's. While the tragic classical tale in dance and music was unfolding of an overpowering great love between Albrecht, the careless youth-princeling masquerading as a commoner, who unwittingly breaks the tender trusting heart of his peasant-girl sweetheart, Giselle, so that she commits suicide, and he, agonizing, comes to mourn at her grave where he is comforted by the sight of her forgiving ghost, Frieda's chilly fingers, still within Gerard's grasp, were commencing to agitate and quiver until they became warm and heated as she followed every movement of the two inspired dancers, Margot Fonteyn, Britain's own ballerina supported by the young Nureyev, late of the Leningrad State Kirov ballet.

Though Gerard's understanding of ballet in all its entrancing intricacies was limited, as a mere spectator he also was held spell-bound by the virtuosity of these two brilliant performers.

Between the acts when the house-lights were on, Frieda withdrew herself deeper into the box in the shadow of its side-curtain. The faint buzz of conversation from all over the theatre reached them in the small elevated box high up amongst the second tier, but she seemed oblivious of where they were. From the far-awayness of her expression she might have fallen into a trance. He did not attempt to break into her detachment. His own attitude of mind was reverential.

So was the spontaneous action made by the young Russian male dancer, when, during a final stupendous curtain-call, the ballerina took a rose from the bouquet that had been handed to her and gave it to him. He dropped to his knees and knelt in adoration and obeisance at her feet.

Then at last the applause was stilled and the curtains came down, not to be raised again. Frieda stood up, fastening the huge garnet-studded button of her purple velvet cape.

'Would you like to go behind?' asked Gerard. 'I will take you round and wait for you outside.'

'No. I know what it means for that supreme one on a night like this. There will be too many pressing to be received and she will have had my little gift which will convey more to her than any words can speak. The French language expresses best what are my feelings.' Frieda touched her throat. ' "*Je suis jusque là*". I am full up to there. Let us drive straight back to my suite at the hotel, my dear. I am truly thankful you were able to be with me sharing in the spirit of that so-wonderful experience. I could not have borne the proximity of anyone else. We shall never be able to repeat it. My conversation is returning. I was dumbfounded, planet-struck, transported. Soon I shall have so many words overflowing in a hurry. Check me, if you please, if I become monotonous, though I do not think I could be when I am discussing what we have seen. How supreme can true art be when it streams through its interpreters who are aware that it proceeds from the God within themselves!'

As soon as they were in the lounge of her private suite redolent with the sweet scent of the lilacs he had brought, Frieda inquired what he would like for supper.

'No need to trouble about me,' he assured her. 'I did as you advised. Before I came I had a very full meal of salt beef, dumplings and carrots at the Cheshire Cheese, and they serve it up as nowhere else in London. I had missed out lunch. Most of us Fleet Street fellows get caught up with the beer-tankards, our jobs in hand and what's on. The break does us good and we very often forget to eat we're so busy yarning away. Cheese and a snack over the counter sometimes is enough, but you haven't had anything at all this evening.'

'Not since the morning. As I told you, from this morning until tomorrow morning I eat nothing. What I have been looking on was food for my spirit, though my figure does not need to reduce its measurements. I am one of those who do not change my inches.'

'You are so slim and small I don't suppose you eat enough to feed a mouse at any time!'

'Occasionally I think I eat less than a mouse. The mouse is a hungry creature. My appetite, only needing so little because there was so little and what little there was had to be shared, stems from those starvation years in Berlin, when nobody had enough, and I can tell you the emptiness in the stomach was not a pleasant sensation. In these times when one goes about to the restaurants amongst the rich gastronomes I may commence to enjoy something that is before me on my plate until it comes up before me that even today there are so many countries in this world where there is trouble and fighting, such a lot of peoples of all colours shooting and killing, and hunger and want in such a degree. Then my appetite is gone and I cannot finish the rest. After my second husband died I had little money once again, and although I have since continued to work hard and make it, I do not wish to save anything except to live as I go. I give it away to the poor. Gaby de Lys, that great little artist, she did the same. It is much more satisfying to know that my money is buying meals and clothes for poor persons deprived of all comforts, and children especially. Who wants to conserve money? Pah! not Frieda Bloch. Money is the poison which corrupted the world from that bad moment when the first coins were made and released for circulation. If you want to know what God thinks of money you have only to look at the men who amass it. I think in that way. So did Nemo, my papa, who was born so poor. After he became the famous clown when the circuses paid him a grand salary he would always be giving to anybody in trouble. "To be miserly is not to be able to laugh", he would say. Laughter was his coinage and the joy of children at his joking his richest reward. We will drink to his memory tonight when you have opened the champagne I ordered to be sent up in readiness, as well as to the stars who have delighted us tonight with their glorious interpretations. Over there on the sideboard – will you uncork it, Gerard, please. Fill up the glasses to the brim. The bubbles have their own ballet, do you see?'

While Gerard was pouring the champagne, Frieda stretched herself on the rug before the fire, completely relaxed.

'A cushion for your head?' he asked.

'No, thank you. This is the attitude of repose between the ballet exercises to lie like this, flat just for a few moments, until the producer calls one to spring up and energize again.

Bring my glass to me here. I can drink in this position without spilling a drop. See? Lovely! We must finish the bottle between us before you leave. Wine is right for us tonight. Sit in that chair opposite me. Shall we first drink our toasts in silence, pausing between each one to let our thoughts speak?'

When, after the pauses, her glass was empty, she held it out for Gerard to refill.

'And now for you – a wish nearest to your heart that it may come true.'

Gerard raised his glass.

'My wish – to you. For your happiness.'

'Such a good wish, but do not make it for me only. Let us enlarge it to drink down all unkindness and all misery and for all to be happy. Sometimes I think that could happen if it is discovered through space-travel that the other planets are inhabited by beings who are all full of love for each other and there is no hatred or greed, envy or killing, so that this sad, muddled, troubled little earth of ours will come to appreciate how far behind it is, and happiness will dawn and remain, and all peoples will come to see what fools they have been. It could be so simple.'

Frieda jumped up with a lissom, resilient bound. 'The effervescence of the wine bubbles has travelled downwards to my feet instead of to my head. I am in the rejoicing mood of Giselle in the first act when she was dancing with such rapture and abandonment to joy after love had displayed his dazzling bird of paradise blue plumage before her and her ecstasy made it seem she was in the pulse-beat of creation. I want to throw off these long clinging lilac draperies for the skirts of a ballerina. They impede me. Would you laugh at me if I were to dress up?'

'Laugh at you! I would delight to see you!'

65

'Then I will do it. I have all of a ballerina's costume with me, that is amongst my stage wardrobe when I am travelling, though I have not worn it since I was in London for a short time years ago as a student in the school of ballet I attended to discover if it was possible to overcome my accident disability. My ballet mistress had been famous before she founded her school in this country on her retirement. She was fully aware of my ambition and the physical hurts I had sustained which had checked it. How indefatigably she worked and interested herself in me as if I was her only pupil! The ballet dress which I will never part with was given to me by her, but eventually we both knew I must bow to the inevitable. The cracks in a piece of broken china that is in many pieces can be skilfully repaired so that they cannot be noticed, but never can it be perfect as it was before, and so with broken bones. When I said "Goodbye" to dear Madame she held me closely in her arms and wrote down on a little screw of paper some words which she said might help and they have helped so very much. These words:'

Frieda repeated them as one might say a prayer:

' "*Dear God give me serenity to accept the things that cannot be changed.*

Give me courage to change the things that can and should be changed,

And give me the wisdom to distinguish one from the other."

'When my heart is faint I say them over to sustain myself. Now I will dance for you. Yes, I want to dance! In that recess under the radiogram you will find several records, the Giselle orchestration amongst them which I bought a few days ago. It is all on the same disc. Please adjust it in readiness for the first movement. I will be with you in a few moments. Then switch on as I enter.'

66

Gerard did so. He waited. Frieda had half-closed the door between the lounge and her bedroom. He could hear her quick flitting movements and little gay snatches of song she was humming to herself like a bird when it commences to trill in the early dawn of a Spring morning.

The door was swung aside and she was there in the frothy ballerina dress and shimmering flesh-pink tights, a wreath of rosebuds in her hair, standing poised and upright on the points of her satin dancing shoes, her arms upraised, finger-tips pressed lightly together over her head.

Gerard switched on the music. A sylph, a naiad flitted into the room. To watch her poetic movements as she danced was to marvel and be thrilled at the spontaneous expression of the rapture she was portraying of the maiden Giselle, transported by love into a seventh heaven of beatitude.

The dance movement was still recording on the revolving disc, the needle about midway towards the finish when, without any warning or signs of fatigue, as she was executing a brilliant whirling *entrechat* it seemed as if a flower had suddenly snapped and broken upon its stalk. It was not a collapse attributable to any lack of technique. For a moment he thought it was a pause, a part of the act, before flinging herself into another movement.

She sank forward, her face covering her hands, on a level with the floor. Did she need his aid to help her to rise? She was near enough for him to touch her but he abstained, divining that some profound emotion was overmastering her. Was she praying or weeping, or both, perhaps?

The disc recording concluded. He switched off and lifted it from its pin, quietly getting up and replacing it amongst the others.

When he turned back from the recess Frieda was sitting

up. The depths of her feelings had gone far beyond the relief of tears, but the piteous expression on her face told him all and more.

So very quiet was her voice:

'In that little while I was not here. I saw a ballerina who had no patched-up broken ankle or an instep so crushed she could never dance to last for one first act without the recurrence of a weakness as you have just seen when sudden pain stabs through the injured foot and there can be no continuation. The dance is ended.'

She pushed up the corners of her mouth resolutely.

' "Pick up and smile" is the ballerina's drill. Do not be sorry for me. I am all right. I am fine. To meet a challenge and to fight with all one's might is right, but if an un-foreseen disaster is the strongest opponent, it is also honour-able to accept defeat as a victory. Let us finish our wine. Then say good night to me, dear Gerard. I have a wish to be alone, not to repine, but to think over our lovely evening.'

12

AFTER three days of fragrant loveliness the lilacs in the flower-basket he had given to her were still fresh and blooming, Gerard remarked when he next called to see Frieda.

'They are in good health, yes. Flowers respond like persons who have the need to be looked after. I have been nursing them with special care to keep them in good health, splitting the stalks and dampening the moss with an aspirin dissolved in water poured over it, and then saying to them, "Live, lilacs, live!" as my young doctor first-husband exhorted me to live when I was in such a wishing-to-fade state in the American Military Hospital, although everything possible was being done for me in the way of care and kindness, patience and skill. That is where I paused in my memoirs I was recounting to you, is it not? Must I continue to look back? To hold a post-mortem over the mistakes one has made in the past is not wholesome, but I can say honestly I have no regrets of that kind. I did my best with the second-best which is the hard lesson I had to learn, like learning to walk again after I had been so long in the plaster casings unable to move for so many weeks, but there were some marvellous compensations I experienced which were given to me in sleep. A psychologist might have some profound Freudian interpretation of those dreams, but my own explanation of them satisfies and assures me that they were heaven-sent. It is my belief that earth has no trouble which heaven cannot heal.'

'What a beautiful belief!'

'And such beautiful dreams! When Jesus was alone in the Garden of Gethsemane and He was overcome by the pre-knowledge of his trial and crucifixion, we are told that He was comforted by angels, and so I think with all human suffering there are the angels sent to comfort afflicted persons in hospital as there must have been for the tortures of those who lived in the hell of concentration camps. Even though they do not see them, the angels must be close at hand when blessed sleep closes the eyes, thus sustaining them to meet yet another day.'

'Describe your dreams.'

'There were several of various kinds, and they were all connected with the use of my feet. One dream was that I was skipping with a rope so tirelessly and effortlessly and another that I was running up a steep mountainside with the utmost ease where there were boulders and stones and the ground was rough. I was bounding over the boulders, and the stones felt like velvet they were so soft and smooth as I trod upon them. And I would dream of dancing as lightly as if I was a puff-ball blown by the wind! I can still dream, though only if I have been profoundly moved, as on Wednesday evening when I was dancing in here after we had returned and so quickly the foot pains cut me short and I could not continue. When I went to bed I could not sleep for such a long time, but when I did what do you think my dream was? I was on the stage at Covent Garden. I was myself the *ballerina assoluta* and I was dancing according to my own interpretation of Giselle. I was dancing all of the three acts with such rapidity of the small steps of *batterie*, executing the long line of the *arabesque* and on to the very end without any pause between the acts. Not once did I falter. I felt as weightless as a space-traveller. Even when I was portraying the sad finale, there was no sensation of heaviness in my feet. I had become the ghost of the light-hearted Giselle whose heart had become unbroken and who was still loving and beloved by the lover she had forgiven. Do you not feel sure an angel dropped that dream into my subconsciousness like a tiny white feather from one of his wings?

'Now I am reaching that stage in my history when the physiotherapy treatment was teaching me to walk again, first with two crutches, after that with two short sticks with rubbers on their ends, then one stick only until, at last, I was walking without any artificial aid. It was very wearisome. Bill Corbett, my young doctor-friend, lightened my long hours coming to sit and talk with me whenever he could spare a few moments. I soon discovered what a wonderful person he was; all his experiences in those days of slaughter and suffering had even more firmly dedicated him to his profession of research-work and healing. He was as devoted and high-minded an idealist as Dr. Schweitzer and if he had been spared I am certain his name would have been upon the medical scroll of great honour.

'At last the time was approaching when I should be discharged from hospital. Bill was greatly concerned what was going to happen to me because I would not be strong enough to attend upon the customers at the café where I had been entertaining. He said that kind of life was not for me any more and I should not remain in Berlin. I must be protected and cared for.

'Then he unfolded the proposal he had been thinking out, and I must tell you that it took my breath away, for it proved to me how entirely good he was to be ready to take up such a heavy responsibility as myself if I would accept his proposal and leave all for him to arrange.

'His plan was immediate marriage. His religious faith was the same as mine. He was a Catholic, and he had already sought the advice of a priest who was able to arrange the ceremony by a special licence and there would be no difficulty about that. It could be on the same day that I left hospital. Then he said the necessary facilities to proceed to England would be simple once I had the status of his wife. On short leave he would fly over with me, and arrange for me to stay in a small hotel in Bayswater. He had stayed there before and the atmosphere was peaceful and quiet. The wife of the proprietor had been a refugee from Hitler Germany he had married before the war, and that should also make me feel not like a stranger. Having brought me over, he would immediately fly back to his quarters to make formal application while he was still serving for transference to an American Military Hospital in London, so that I would not have to wait very long, perhaps for not more than a week by myself. Following upon that we would be together while he was obtaining his discharge, when we could proceed to America. There he had a post waiting for him that he would be able to step into immediately, in a hospital where he would be engaged upon research for the killer diseases of cancer and leukemia.

'He thought his sister, Nancy, who was older than himself, would be pleased to share her house with us, and it would be a very comfortable arrangement for us all. He said she was a dear person, with a most vital presence and so many interests outside herself by which she gave up much of her life to helping anyone who might be in need of solicitude and care. She had no time to be lonely after she became widowed. As soon as we were married he would be writing her a long letter explaining all about ourselves, and the circumstances which had brought us together. He was quite certain she would be entirely sympathetic. By the way he spoke I could see how fond he was of her, and I could also discern what a similarity there was in their two natures, both so concentrated upon the well-being and care of those in need, troubled, ill-health or any kind of distress. It is a marvellous experience when as we proceed through life we come into contact with such persons whose hearts are pure gold.

'What were my feelings when my Bill made this suggestion to me? I was overwhelmed and overcome. One consideration I voiced to him when my emotion would allow me to speak. His self-forgetful magnanimous proposal which was enough to take any girl's breath away in a situation like this. Was it made out of his chivalrous desire to protect and provide me with an anchorage? Not only was I so young, but he also had to consider he might meet someone he loved very much who would be complementary to himself, and whose interests and training might be allied to his own calling? Then, as well as a responsibility to him, I should be a burden to him, because what was I except a little Polish-German dancer he had met in a Berlin café, not educated in any degree and speaking the English language in a most imperfect manner.

'He took my hand and held it very warmingly as he gave me his answer. How well I remember!

' "Listen to me, Fairy!" he said. "You could never be anything other than a beloved burden, a little piece of thistledown that has floated deep down into my heart and got stuck there from the very first moment I saw you dancing. I love you, and I shall love you always. Trust me, Fairy. I don't ask or expect you to love me in the same way as I love you. After all you have been through your need is the gentleness of love, not its transports. For the time being until we have got ourselves sorted out, although I shall be your husband in name you will think of me as your big brother. That's all I ask. Once I have got you away with me to America you shall have all the after-treatment and skill that the highest of our medical profession can give to you. I want you to be able to dance again, Fairy!"

'What could I say? I was wordless again.

'I carried his dear hand to my lips and pressed my kisses into his palm, and then I held it under my cheek resting upon the pillow, and he remained with me until it was time to continue his round of the hospital.'

13

'I HAVE not reached the end of this short sequence in my life history,' Frieda resumed. 'If one considers it, the course of a television play as it is being produced on the floor of the studio has much of a similarity with ourselves as we proceed through life upon the studio floor of this existence. It is of such unbounded dimensions that none of us, whether we are in the crowd or with bit-parts, or even the principals in this vast enactment, are able to see the Producer. He is withdrawn to the higher place above where He can witness what is going on and what has to be done. There is no detail that escapes Him and if we slacken or are careless He does not lose His patience. Only if we keep our senses alert and our ears attuned to hear the still, small voice when it reaches us through the megaphone of God which we call conscience down here, we do not make so many mistakes. The play has been devised and written, and the author and director and producer are the three in one who combine all purposes. How should we expect to understand, criticise or rebel against the intricacies of a construction which is within their control and by whom we should be controlled? Oh, yes, especially as I grow older and when I am alone I have my own thoughts which strengthen me a lot and hold me back from despairing at those times when I have been working very hard and my health does not feel equal to the task. At such times the small voice whispers to me giving me the unmistakable direction: "Be still and do not move."

'Now I will tell you what happened and how I became a widow within a week of my marriage to Bill.

'He had made every arrangement with such thoughtful attention to detail there were no hitches or delays.

'I felt our marriage was a truly religious union as it was solemnised in the small Catholic Church he attended regularly. A wonderful feeling it was as we came out of the church to know that I belonged to someone who would love and care for me until death parted us. How soon that finality would overtake us – how could one envisage such a calamity?

'Before he left me the day after he had flown me over and placed me in the good hands of the hotel proprietor and Paula, his wife, with whom I became friends on the instant, Bill took me to the branch of a London bank close by and arranged with the manager for a deposit of some money and a small current account in my name, and I was given a cheque book for myself after I had written my signature. It was for two hundred pounds which seemed a most extravagant amount to me, for I had no intentions of spending his money on anything that was not necessary. He had already told me his circumstances and I knew he was not rich. His parents having died while he was of school age, his sister had attended to his education and fees at college until he had graduated. When the Americans joined in the War he had just qualified and commenced on his medical career when he was called up. All he had was his Army pay and no other money except what he would be earning as a doctor when he took up his research work at the hospital in California.

'What did his lack of wealth signify to me who had never had any? How rich was I in his love! I was more well off than if I had been the wife of a millionaire. I had never been so happy since those days when I had been the circus-baby, Nemo's two eyes, the darling of his heart.

'Feeling assured of his quick return in a few days, saying goodbye for such a short while held no anxiety or anguish for me. I had only to look forward to the telephone message which would tell me to be there to meet him at the Airport when his transfer to London had been effected. He had already made his application and it had been granted. All our plans seemed so perfect. How could anything possibly go wrong?

'The five days after he had left passed pleasantly and quickly enough because I busied myself helping Paula, the wife of the proprietor, doing such small sitting-down domestic jobs as I was able to do, preparing vegetables for cooking, cleaning silver and things like that and conversing together in our own tongue as we worked.

'Then without any warning, and to my surprise. I was paid a visit by one of Bill's best friends whom I had already met when they came together to the café. He had come to impart some official news to me, but for compassionate reasons he had been given forty-eight hours leave to bring and break it to me. It was the news of Bill's sudden death.

'When he was telling me I could not at first believe it. It seemed like some part of a nightmare out of which I would awaken to find life was just the same with the future all so bright at last after those agonies and terrors of war.

'This so calamitous incident was a misadventure which might be described as one in a thousand.

'Bill and his friend had gone out into the country for a spin on push-bicycles which they had hired. Coming back into the city, Bill's friend was slightly ahead of him. Bill had stopped and got off to make some adjustment to his

77

bicycle-lamp as it was about lighting-up time, and from a cinema further down the street the audience of the first house was coming out, amongst them some young boys who were proceeding in a mad zig-zag fashion on bicycles. Bill had just remounted and was coming on when his friend turned round to look and see how far he was behind, and at that moment he saw the accident happen before his eyes. Coming round the corner one of these young lads doing the wobble ran straight into Bill's bicycle, and Bill was thrown over the handle-bars in some kind of twist to the ground, where he lay still. His friend told me he was not unconscious, but that he knew he had sustained a severe spinal injury. In the ambulance he whispered to his friend that he could not move or feel his limbs from the back of his neck down.

'The same evening it was all over. His neck was broken.

'That was the end of Bill's life at twenty-five and the end of my world for a long, long time, but I had to continue.

'I had no will or wish to continue, but I knew it would be Bill's wish that I should. When standing by my bedside he had called me back from the shadows so I knew I would not be worthy of him if I was not brave enough to go on by myself alone.

'His friend had brought a small package containing some of Bill's personal belongings which he gave to me that I might care to look through when I could feel composed enough.

'Later on, I steeled myself to do so. There was a diary full of medical notes and a bundle of photographs, snapshots taken in California. His wallet was in it, very neat and tidy. In one of its partitions there was inserted a little curl of my hair he had asked me for and I had given to him the day he left. Also within the wallet was a letter addressed to his sister, but not stuck up. Ought I to read it before stamping and posting it on? I thought it might be best. There were several pages of it on thin airmail sheets and it was the long letter he had told me he was going to write informing her of our marriage and his plans to return with me to California when his medical corps duties released him. He had evidently not had time to finish it because it came to an end in the middle of a sentence as if he had been called away and intended to resume.

'The lines ran into each other as I was reading it, and can you wonder? I hesitated to post this unfinished letter. I asked myself whether it was right to add to her grief when she was informed of his death, by telling her of my sadness as well and my own unsettled state. I decided it was best not so I kept it. His letter opened by saying this would be a long one to make up for so many short ones because he had been so fully occupied, but now he had a matter of great moment to him of which she should be the first to be told. How eagerly he said he was awaiting the day when he would be coming back to California with his Fairy-wife, and how sure he was there would be such love between all three of us. He described me as I appeared to him when he first saw me. He said he did not think I could be real. I did not look like a cabaret dancer-hostess-entertainer in a hide-out night-club. I looked as if I had come out of a forest dingle where I had been dancing in a ring amonst the other fairies, but somehow a puff of wind must have blown me into the café. What he had written was like a piece of poetic imagery which one would not expect from someone who was chiefly concerned with writing medical reports and pre-scriptions. I have read and re-read that letter so often and slept with it under my cheek because his hand had been moving over the page as he was writing it, and I like to

79

think it was still his hand as on that day in hospital when he had asked me to marry him and I had kissed his palm and carried it under my cheek. It made me feel near to him and comforted me.

'Had I ever been truly in love with Bill? My friend, I was so young. After all these years between, I can only think of his good face, his fair hair, his glowing complexion of health and vigour, his manliness, his kindness and overflowing goodness.

'Every morning and every night of my life ever since I have spoken his name with a blessing added to it in my prayers, and I do not feel he is in any way remote from me.'

14

REHEARSALS for the 'Crimson Ramblers', America's latest and most popular imported musical straight from Broadway, with its galaxy of picked talent surrounding Frieda Bloch, its foremost woman star, had been in progress for the past week, extending very often into the late afternoon because such a vast production needed pruning and adaptation for its London presentation at the Pall Mall Theatre. In consequence the unfolding of her most intimate life-history to Gerard had been held up and he had not seen her during what had seemed to him a long interval of time, although he had telephoned her each evening to find out when it would be possible to resume their talks.

So very far off was her voice on the last occasion that he could scarcely hear it.

'Hold on a second. This must be a bad line. I'll get myself put through to another.'

She stopped him.

'The line is all right. I can hear you perfectly. The fault is not the line, it is myself. I am so tired, you see, and my chest troubles me a little.'

'Your chest?' He was immediately concerned. 'Have you caught a chill? Are you ill?'

'A small cold, perhaps. The cold, damp London air when Spring is so long delayed as it is this year, does not agree with me. If I talk any more louder I shall cough, so I conserve my breath. Don't worry. It is only the slightest touch of bronchitis. It must not be that I croak like a frog on the night when I have to sing, so I have gone straight to my bed with my electric blanket turned on. Tomorrow, as it is Sunday, I will not get up at all. I will not even invite you to come and see me, much as I would like to in case it induces me to talk which would not be your fault, but my own.'

'You should send for a doctor.'

'I have a doctor who tells me what I should do when it is needful from the distances that can be transmitted on the radio line which is quite definite between heaven and where we are. It was my Bill who first detected this lung weakness when I was in the American Military hospital under his care. It comes from the early days when I was in Berlin and the war was in its fullest rage. Don't be troubled, my dear. I am used to it. In America and other places when the attacks have been severe the doctors have given me gold injections before I could go on the stage, but this little infection is a minor complaint and it will be cleared up by Monday. Do you care to fetch me?'

'Monday? Yes, rather! What time?'

'A quarter-to-seven so that we can be leisurely if that is not too early for you.'

'Never too early to be with you!'

'You flirt over the telephone! I did not think that you had the disposition of a flirt! Be serious, you naughty boy!'

'I am entirely serious – never more so. As for flirtation, I've never been inclined that way. I've been far too occupied with my work. Frieda, are you quite sure you wouldn't like me to come round to see you now, tonight? You know I would put anything and everything aside to be with you.'

'No, my dear, thank you. I know my disposition. Good-night, dear friend.'

Gerard put down the receiver reluctantly. His anxiety for her refused to be dismissed.

At half-past six on Monday evening, he called for her.

'I'm afraid I'm rather early,' he apologized. 'Don't let me hurry you.' He could not fail to notice how very fragile and pale she looked. 'How are you?' he asked concernedly. 'I was tempted to ring you up on Sunday, but I refrained as I thought it was more important not to disturb you.'

'You are such a considerate person. I am much better, thank you. It was such a day of glorious sunshine. What a contrast is your English weather! It is no wonder that those who are too poor to travel into the sun as the birds do have a dolorous nature. Yesterday was so different from the day before. I wide-opened my window and the sun streamed right on to my bed so I lay there as if I were a basking cat. It was a most delicious rest after those endless rehearsals when I have to be on stage almost continuously all the way through. Never mind, I am no longer tired. All I am experiencing now is the butterflies.'

'Feeling nervous, you mean?'

'Always at the commencement there are black butterflies in my tummy stamping about wearing heavy shoes with nails in them like the tap dancers. There are my quickened heart-flutterings, but once the curtain is up and I am on, they fly out, and their wings have changed to a beautiful blue colour. That is what it means to be in a profession from which one feels one would like to finish and retire and leave it for always, and at other times when it is getting nearer to the hour when one should be in the dressing-room putting on the grease paint, it seems that there is no other life to compare with it, and the restless feeling is the same as is felt by the person with itchy feet who cannot remain in one place. With Nemo, my papa, it was exactly the same, though occasionally he liked to rest his caravan and say he would prefer to remain amongst the lilacs and forests in the joyful country of Austria. It is never wise for a person in a settled occupation to think there could be a successful link-up with an entertainer. The links are weak and they break easily.'

'But when people in show business link up the links do not seem to last very long either, do they?'

'That is too true, and the usual reason for such discontents is caused by professional jealousies, if one has more success than another and the other gets left behind in the rat-race, so they try again with someone else. Do you think we should be starting now? Would you not like a drink first? Are you sure? Then let us go. Will you carry this little basket for me very carefully? I am in a trembling condition before the butterflies are liberated and I do not want to drop it and smash them. There are fresh eggs inside. What do I want with eggs in my dressing-room? Let me tell you. I make a little hole with a needle in the egg and I suck it before I go on and if my throat is getting dry because of the nervous feeling every artiste knows. It is much more efficacious than the many kinds of pep pills which can turn one into a drug-addict. There are more who are in the grip of drugs than any other colony and fortunes are made by those evil ones who peddle them.'

Gerard held her coat for her.

'You will be amongst the bogy-men in front in a bunch, I suppose?' Frieda asked. 'That is my name for the critics, who can be most severe. Criticism if it is fair can be very good medicine for an artist, but so many bogies are inclined to be destructive because some private events have soured their dispositions. Some do not take into consideration that criticism is easy, but art difficult. I have no grumble against any myself, because if anything they have over-praised me.'

'I shall not be in the front. I am coming to see you, not to criticize.'

'Then you have no reserved seat? Why did you not tell me?'

'Because there are none to be reserved. I made enquiries this morning. The theatre is booked right up for a month ahead. I shall slip in where I can, into the gallery most likely, or into the back of the pit if it is standing room only. I am not on my job tonight. I asked the Chief to send another man instead. After the show I'll be ready with my car and drive you to the party at the Savoy and I'll fetch you again when its over.'

'I shall not be present at the celebration, so we can drive straight back to my apartment where we will have supper very quietly together and resume our delayed talk in a comfortable manner.'

'But you will be expected, surely?'

'I have made the other arrangements. I have conspired with my good, kind agent, Al Parker, to find a reasonable excuse for me. He will be present himself, and my absence will afford the opportunity to make some good advance publicity for Jennie Williams when she makes her speech for me.'

'And who is Jennie Williams?'

'She is the one who will so shortly be stepping into my rôle. Al Parker was on holiday in a small village in Cornwall when he saw her performance at a concert party and arranged her contract as quickly as he does such things. Al never mistakes or delays. For all of us he acts for in the profession he behaves like the captain of a ship, with complete authority, but a benevolent attitude which has earned him the affectionate nickname of Pal amongst ourselves, and so many of us have reason to thank him for the battles he has fought for us, declaring what we should be paid and what we are worth to the money-men. It was last summer he spotted Jennie and he lost no time in making the right arrangements for her. She is so pretty and charming, with the natural pure singing voice of a nightingale and no ambitions to marry a millionaire or to be possessed of mink coats or stealable jewels. Her home is in a poor district that has lost its better days. I have been to visit her parents. Her father is a gassed soldier living on a disability pension, and her mother, until Jennie was beginning to earn and contribute, used to go out to do cleaning for two shillings-and-sixpence an hour. Jennie's big wish is that she may succeed and be able to buy a house for them in a pleasant locality with some comforts to make life easier for them now they are getting older. One afternoon I would like to ask Jennie to tea and introduce her to you so that, after she has made her first West End appearance and if your journalistic integrity makes it allowable, you might find it convenient to bring her before the cameras in television.'

'I could certainly make the suggestion if I think as a subject she had genuine interest for my special feature as an interviewer.'

'Thank you, Gerard, and that is enough. It is the squareness of your character that established our instant friendship. When you meet Jennie I am quite sure you will perceive she has the qualities of a Julie Andrews, or one like Vera Lynn or Gracie Fields whose audience-appeal can never grow stale or less because the musical sounds, *the timbre*, the feeling comes out of their throats straight up from their hearts. It is a gift of some divine nature. How can I describe it?

'This world of entertainment, as it occurs to me, there is not so much difference between the way success can arrive to those in show business or to those who may be writers, painters or any who divert the public by presenting themselves in one way or another. It is one of two things to succeed in my opinion. To be veritable and sincere is to wish to give something that is deeply within oneself and to make it as perfect as possible, and in that there is the greatest reward and satisfaction. For others it may be what I call a "freak hit" with perhaps no talent whatever in the freakishness, but something that is twisted and wild and ungoverned which the wild and ungoverned and freakish respond to as the jungle animals follow the cries of their own species. In these days the cries seem to predominate and the jungle is very close. The little Jennie-girl, my understudy, she has worked incessantly from the time she was a child-artist taking her first lessons in the Conti School where your so famous Noel Coward graduated into the master he is today with talents in so many directions, though he wears no frills. Peter Ustinov is another. I am a very proud person to be able to say that their names are in my little red book.'

'What is your little red-book?'

'It is in my handbag, a little notebook in which, from time to time, I have written down the names of people I can't forget because I never want to forget, commencing with my dear Papa, the *auguste* of the circus ring and some of those who befriended me in the terrible days of Berlin, and the name of the nurse in the American Military hospital who showed me how to look in the mirror and smile. In

87

England since I have arrived here on this visit I have added one name only because I shall often wish to recall it after I have gone away. Gerard Hemming, your name. You are a very much occupied person with so much on your plate between your television interviews and your writings for your newspaper, that I am gratified you wished to see me again after I had said I was not willing to be interviewed for the television. Celebrities on toast would be my name for it.'

'My dear little friend! If only I could make you understand how the bottom has fallen out of these last few days for me while you've been kept so busy at rehearsal and so tired afterwards that I haven't been able to come and see you. If only—'

They had been walking slowly along the long corridor towards the lift. Gerard checked himself. Now was not the appropriate moment to obtrude his innermost personal feelings when her first-night appearance in London in the latest American hit was so imminent.

He rang the lift-bell for the attendant without completing his sentence.

15

IT was a whimsy of Gerard's after he had parked his car to attach himself to the end of the long queue which had early commenced to gather and swell and grow, and to pick up any stray tags of conversation passing between those already assembled patiently waiting for pit doors and gallery entrance to open.

The stray tags of conversation drifted to him, Cockney accents prevailing. He kept his ears open for Frieda's name amongst the stars under desultory discussion.

'Benny Manhattan. 'E was over on the Telly not long ago. Makes up 'is jokes as 'e goes along, pickin' the British to pieces. 'E said that our Prime Minister had got a dial like a melting wax-work. I don't call that comical. Joked about Prince Philip and Princess Margaret and Lord Snowdon. Called them by their Christian names as if they 'adn't got the right to any title in front. Then he stands still with a face like a dead-pan after 'e's made a joke if you can call it a joke and waits for the laughs. There's too many Yanks comin' over here showin' themselves off. I bet though 'e's top of the bill wherever 'e goes; there's nothin' 'e can do that beats our own Benny Hill. Our Benny 'e can be right down funny on 'is own without draggin' in names of folks what don't deserve to be guyed.'

'Ay! Benny Hill. 'E's a prize. Except for our Benny there's not any to beat 'im for bringin' out the belly-laughs on the Telly. Changin' 'mself over into someone else what can't be recognized as the same chap, dressed differently ten times or more in 'alf an hour takes a bit of doin'. And that smile of 'is when 'e looks out and nods to say "see yer next week", 'e might be in the room the way 'e does it.'

'Same as 'er we've come to see tonight. Changes 'erself into someone else in front of your eyes without so much as changin' her costume she's wearing. She's got the whole bag-full. Nothin' she can't do. She dances, makes you laugh and cry. She's one of us.'

'One of us. How can she be? She's a foreigner, ain't she?'

'Foreigner or not, it don't signify. She's for all of us soon as she comes on with that little smile of hers, holdin' 'er 'ands out as if she was wanting to shake hands with everyone. The whole 'ouse seems to light up although the lights 'ave been doused. You can't put a name to it.'

'Doors open. Come on, mate. It ain't arf parky out 'ere. What's come over this climate with the Grand National bein' run in a snow-storm unless it's Russia tryin' the great freeze on us. It's the cold war turned into ice.'

'Ay! Fings ain't what they used to be.'

'That's the name of a play!'

'S'true enough!'

The patient queue commenced to move in and Gerard managed to edge himself into a gangway seat in the last row of the pit. For the last to come in, it was standing room only. It was close on the moment for curtain-up and the electrical excitement of a first night pervaded the packed house.

Quite apart from his intense personal regard for her, Gerard was amazed by the brilliance and virtuosity of the performance she put over, so perfectly timed and adjusted to the whole that not any of the other artists who might be involved in a scene with her were rendered any the less because she was superlative.

Whatever the early trials, forlorn childhood and harsh experiences in her private life had been, her stage personality emitted a sparkling effervescence which epitomized zest and joy.

In this British importation of America's latest musical in which two completely adjusted composers of songs and lyrics had collaborated in harmonious unison as melodious and ear-catching as had been the happy combination between Gilbert and Sullivan of the Edwardian days, Frieda assumed not one but several rôles, displaying an impressionistic versatility that was beyond analysis or criticism. She was as dexterous as a juggler who never falters or faults, but continues to manipulate his objects with apparently pliant effortlessness. In one of her frocks which was spangled with iridescent mother o'pearl sequins her own scintillating performance was as if she was a human sequin herself.

Her singing voice, though of small range, was clear, sweet and bell-like as befitted the daintiness of her fairy-like figure, her toe-dancing interludes, timed not to last more than a few moments, epitomized sheer poetry of motion. She seemed to be giving so much, and in such full measure, withholding nothing. Like the rest of the audience he was entranced, spell-bound.

When the finale was reached it seemed as if the ovation would never cease and the curtain was raised again and again. She took no bows for herself. Each time it went up she put out her hand to bring forward some other artist, as if including her or him in her own measure of success.

Bouquets were handed over, so many, so elaborate and in such profusion that they had to be laid in a pile around her feet after she had received them. Amongst them was the simple one he had ordered to be delivered, a sheaf of the white and purple lilacs that were her favourite flowers. When finally the curtain went up for the last time, the bouquet she was holding was his. She was pressing her face amongst the blooms, and when she raised it, she was weeping and smiling at the same time, the rainbow personification as it came to him of Spring with its simultaneous showers and sunshine.

What a woman! What a supreme artist!

The theatre emptied and Gerard went round to fetch his car and bring it to the stage door exit. She would no doubt be besieged by many pressing for dressing-room interviews and so there was no point in his going back-stage when she would be anxious to hasten away.

Now the artists were beginning to emerge. It was a very large cast, the chorus and dancers and smaller part performers being the first to leave, and then the leading players were waylaid by autograph-hunters, mostly eager teenagers, whom they paused to oblige with a hastily written signature. Gradually these dispersed and it seemed that almost all had left except Frieda. The stage-door-keeper, an old white-whiskered man, was reaching for his bunch of keys on the rack in readiness to lock up the back premises.

At last she appeared walking down the dimly-lit passage carrying the bouquet of variegated lilacs, pausing by the ledge of the door-keepers' box-like compartment to rest and open her handbag on it, taking out some small packages which she pushed towards him and he took eagerly, transferring them to his pocket. Hardly any of the rest who had passed the be-medalled veteran had so much as troubled to say more than a careless 'goodnight' to him.

Frieda's surprising action was to lean over the ledge and to kiss him affectionately on both cheeks.

As she turned to move on the old man looked after her, beaming. She had made him happy.

Gerard swung open the car door for her and she was beside him, carefully placing the bunch of lilacs in her lap, her hands holding them protectively as he manoeuvered the small car through the narrow side-turning.

'The old doorkeeper, did you notice him?'

'I did. I saw you kiss him. What made you do that?'

'He has such a likeness to my papa, though he would be much older, of course. He is seventy-three. He has been in two wars. Also he speaks German. I like to give him his favourite tobacco called "Honeydew" which he appreciates most of all. My papa also loved to smoke and puff at his pipe. I am very responsive towards old persons. I can feel their hearts calling out that they want to be loved. Many of them have to be so lonely and it gives them great pleasure to be remembered in such small ways. Gerard, dear, thank you for my lovely lilacs. As soon as they were handed over I guessed they were from you.'

'I am glad you chose to bring them back with you. And what happens to all the tributes you had, enough to fill a taxi? Do you have them sent to a hospital?'

'No, not to a hospital. I never do. In hospital there is never any lack of flowers from friends and relatives visiting, so many the nurses very often cannot find enough vases to put them in. Mine are placed in buckets of water until tomorrow morning when I will fill a taxi with them and drive a little way out of London to Harrow, Middlesex, where there is a country home I have been told about which a most generous professional called Charles Denville made a gift of before he died for old and infirm persons who cannot perform any longer because they have gone past it. To be in an institution that is for the aged, however beneficent, must make them aware that the curtain must soon fall for the last time. I shall take them myself and we will talk what you call in English "shop" together as I sit amongst them. Bouquets for each one of the old ladies. How it will delight them to remember their triumphant days when they had flowers handed to them over the footlights!'

16

THE buffet supper Frieda had ordered to be brought up to her private suite was laid out in readiness for their late return.

Gerard perceived that now she was so weary she could hardly stand. Small wonder after such a sustained performance which would have been a tax on an entertainer of more robust physique, but for one of her extreme fragility the exhaustion following on it was not surprising.

He put his arm around her and led her to the sofa.

'Lie down and rest and let me wait on you. Those eggs you took with you to the theatre to eat raw cannot have done very much to keep you going.'

'Ah! those eggs! They were not for me after all.'

'How's that? I didn't smash any of them, I hope? I thought they were all intact when I handed them over.'

'They were not broken. You see, just now the hens are all very gummed up in their egg-laying and so fresh eggs are expensive and scarce to obtain in the shops. My dresser keeps fowls in her backyard, but they have produced not one egg for several days, and as she has her little daughter returned home after a tonsil operation I insisted that she must take the eggs for her. I have no appetite at present, but please help yourself. What is there? Lobster salad, some liver paté, salami, salmon. If I see you begin to eat I may feel more disposed to have something myself. A bottle of

Liebfraumilch, I see. Some cold *consommé* and *Liebfraumilch*, that will be enough nourishment for me. Do not over-persuade me. I will take little sips and enjoy the quiet lull in here with you after all the hustle and bustle and noise and excitement. The world of the theatre pushes out everything else and when one emerges one feels as if one had left half of oneself back there on the darkened stage.'

Gerard placed a cup of *consommé* and glass of wine on the small table he drew up for her beside the sofa. Then he attended to his own wants seated near by to her with tray on his knees.

Frieda's expression was tranquil.

'How rewarding is friendship which is so within the bonds of harmony that between the silences one can almost hear its music! Little did I imagine that when I came to England for this short while expecting to be quite lonely, that I should open my heart and confide my life-history to a total stranger who has become so near to me. You know, Gerard, you are an experience to me. You are not indifferent. My womanhood makes me aware of that. You are so honourably restrained. It makes me feel sometimes as if I was cheating you because I can give you no more than you will put into my life-story which cannot include ourselves as passionate lovers.'

Gerard made the position between them clear as he felt it himself.

'I love you. I adore you, but first and above all I esteem and honour you. Also I honour my profession. There are times when we journalists may be brought into close touch with someone we have been especially detailed to seek out, as I first came into your orbit. A doctor on entering his profession takes solemn vows. A journalist makes no such vows. There are witch-hunts for front-page stories which should not be. Even royalty is not exempt from this spattering by printer's ink. It makes me feel very hot under the collar when journalists go to such lengths. How are you feeling? Any less tired?'

'I am alerting. The *consommé*, I have finished it, see? And the wine, it is refreshing me. Are you in any haste to return? No? Then if you feel in the disposition to listen to me I would like to resume my interrupted history, or we may lose the sequence of it.'

'I am always eager to listen and I'm in no hurry. Far from it.'

'Then where was it I paused? Wait, I remember. I was in the private, comfortable hotel in Bayswater, where my Bill had left me to fly over to Germany and to come back quickly to join me until he could get his full discharge. I had received the dreadful news of his bicycle accident and sudden death through having his neck broken and the news brought to me to be softened by his brother-officer medical friend. He was very kind. Everybody knew he had been so fond of my Bill. How could he console me? It was not possible.'

'You were stunned. You must have been. You poor child!'

'Yes, I was a little more than a child in those days, but I had to grow-up. I do not think I even cried. My tottering steps took me out first to the little Catholic Church where I said my prayers for him, and lit three little candles before Our Lady. I felt him very near to me. I seemed to hear him say in his downright American way which does not waste words: "Stand up and take it, Fairy." I resolved to be brave because he would wish me to be brave, and I also had the tradition of Nemo behind me.

'Paula, the German wife of the hotel proprietor, she was goodness itself to me. The first night of my bereavement she

97

came to my room and slept in my bed with her arms around me. I felt that I had a mother who cared for me, she was so tender. The proximity of her warm plump body exuded comfort into me.

'Like most German women she was very practical. I would not say I am over-practical myself, but then my blood is mixed and I think there is more of Poland in me than anything else. After a few days she did her best to help, suggest and advise me, because I was then rudderless. I did not know how to steer myself or in what direction, I was so bewildered. She impressed on me I must consider my financial position first of all. I might perhaps be eligible for a widow's pension, but even if that were so I did not wish to make application for any form of support in that way. There was the sum of two hundred pounds Bill had already placed in the bank for me. How should I use it?

'Paula said I might continue to stay with them and pay nothing. She had talked it over with her husband and he was agreeable. If I liked I could assist with the bed-making and little jobs, but nothing more than that and they would be very pleased to have me.

'The little jobs I would be delighted to do in any case. I am fond of domesticity but I could not agree to be a sponge on their kindness, and so I persuaded her to let me remain on at the rate of thirty shillings a week.

'It must have cost a lot more than that when food was still so difficult and expensive and rationed, and every delicacy she could think of she would provide for me to put nourishment and more strength into me before I could attempt to pick up the challenge of life.

'And while I was recovering there again revived in me the greatest longing to be able to study the ballet properly until I was qualified to become the member of a ballet corps, so what did I do but seek out the advice and aid of the greatest teacher who had founded a school of ballet in Britain, Madame Rambert. Today she has the honour to be a Dame of the British Empire, and could anyone deserve it more? What a teacher, what a woman, and what a friend!

'Knowing all about me, my accident and my weakness, she agreed to make the trial with me, and how she laboured to succeed, but as you know, it was not to be, and in the end I had to accept it was unachievable. I would never be able to sustain a continuous ballet performance although I might have the technique, the love for it and the knowledge.'

'What next?'

'Paula advised me again. I still had money in the bank because my superb ballet mistress had refused to accept any fees. Paula's advice was that I should take a full secretarial course of book-keeping and typewriting, to gain myself a certificate that would make me skilled and employable.

She was not unambitious for me. She was extremely sensible, and she thought that with my knowledge of three languages of German, Polish and French as an added qualification I might obtain a responsible post as secretary to an M.P. or some person of importance. She did her best to infuse me with confidence. Profit, she kept on saying to me, was much better than fame. I did not feel I could be any use as a secretary but I made the attempt, but it was a very poor attempt. I paid one term's fees in advance to an accredited college and I found myself in a room with many others and a very precise teacher. She had a most severe disposition and not much patience. I think she took an instant dislike to me and I daresay my sensitivity to her attitude made me slow to learn and stupid. Another thing that upset me when they were all in action at the same time, was the noise of all those typewriters banging and clacking in such rapidity, like machine-gun fire it sounded to me. I had bad headaches and giddiness and in my sleep I would be tapping on the machine nearly all night and wake up very tired.

'No, a secretarial training was not for me. Why must I persevere at doing something I should always detest for my living? I was sure no M.P. would ever find me reliable enough to keep for very long. I was given several interviews, but nobody engaged me. Paula had to agree with me that her advice had been a mistake. She had herself been trained before marriage in a business capacity in Germany and so it was natural she should think the same would be best for me. Now she came to the conclusion that after all my metier could only be in some form of entertainment as the show-business must be in my veins. How to proceed in such a direction she could not tell me, except to mention the films as a possibility.

'After making all kinds of inquiries I discovered that in Shaftesbury Avenue there were a number of offices belonging to various theatrical agents for the stage, variety and films.

'So that is how it happened, in a short while I found myself as a film extra amongst a crowd in Ace Film Productions at Elstree.'

17

THE following afternoon when Gerard called, Frieda was ready to resume the tale of her career and memories. The tea equipage had been brought in and he had arrived punctual to the minute as usual.

'I must not allow too many pauses to come in between,' she said, 'because now the show has commenced, this month will soon be in the can the same as a film when it is finished, and I should hate to leave you not right-up-to-the-moment with my history before I leave. I am not in the least tired today. I am one of those with a great resilience. I may go down, but I am quickly up. The muffins are hot. I toasted them myself a few minutes ago, and here is your tea with the five lumps of sugar. Are you such an unsweetened nature that you prefer so many? You do not appear so to me. I have a very high opinion of your accomplishments. It is no wonder you have achieved a reputation for yourself that is of so high a standard amongst newspaper men.'

'Seventy-five per cent pure luck and the rest a certain amount of ability,' was Gerard's modest estimation of his attainments.

'It is a very clever thing you do nevertheless on television to make the onlookers interested when you are interviewing some person, to wish to see what your front face is like, but no more of you is to be seen as you are placed except the back of your head and your shoulders. The secret I think is your method and the rest is in the quality of your voice. It is a quiet voice that makes one think you must be a good person in spite of your insistent but persuasive directness.'

'Just "one of the blokes" as we speak of each other in Fleet Street amongst ourselves. There's nothing very special about me,' Gerard disclaimed. 'Frieda, I have a boyhood's left-over weakness for buttery muffins. May I help myself to another?'

'Of course. They are all for you. I prefer this brown bread and butter. Now let me take this step back into the years that are gone. How many years? Just over seventeen from 1945 to the present time, and so I make you the confession of my correct age. I shall be thirty-five on the 7th of October of this year. On my birthdays I do not find it so easy to smile into the mirror!'

'Except for the time you have been an idol of the public with your light never dimming, to look at you no one would guess you were a day older than twenty-five – if as much.'

'Ah, but that is only my outward appearance. Within me I am a woman of experience with such a changing background of shifting scenes that I am inclined to lose myself when I am recollecting and reversing the reel. You never make any notes. If you are going to write all this that I am now telling you, how will you remember after I am gone? I mean when I am dead.'

He winced, but he gave her the reassuring answer.

'I am taking mental notes which, according to my way of journalising, is much more reliable than jottings on perforated pieces of flimsy I might tear out and mislay. When I go back to my flat I record it straight away on my typewriter. I must be a human dictaphone because it all comes back even with the sound of the voice; but don't finalise the ending in those sad words. I would like to bring your story right up to the present time and leave it there in the full flower of your triumphs and looking forward to your return in the not far-off future.'

'Do not look so pained, my dear. I would not like to distress you. Death is only a passage through life like walking a bridge. Why should anyone be sad? I think we should all be glad to know that we are sure to meet our mothers and our fathers and our friends. After that we shall go on, I think, to some other condition, to sustain and to inspire, to entertain, or whatever it may be. It will all seem as natural as when we are first born. The most difficult part of existence is when we begin to be perplexed as children and ask so many innocent questions which come into our eager minds, but alas! we are not always given the right answers; so when, later, we find out we have been put off or told lies, we begin to doubt those very persons closest to us in whom we put all our trust. My own dear papa was never like that and I think that is the reason why in spite of all my troubles and vicissitudes I have never doubted God. Now, Gerard, we will continue on a more ordinary journey. Step quickly into the bus with me. It is the studio-bus at Elstree station waiting to convey those who have no luxury transport to the butcher's shop.'

'The butcher's shop?'

'That is how it is spoken of by the insignificant persons of all varieties who congregate in the crowded waiting-rooms and all the way up the stairs of the film agents in Shaftesbury Avenue to seize what is thrown out to them like little pieces of offal when the producers from the film companies ring up the agent to say what they will be requiring for the crowd-scenes. Two guineas a day used to be the rate of pay for all to be ready on the set at eight o'clock in the morning until five or six in the afternoon. The pay is for a higher amount nowadays, though it would mean no more because of the high cost of living. The bar and the canteen takes a heavy proportion out of the pay-envelope and the Welfare State insurance stamps with the agent's ten per cent which he takes off.

'If I had the ability and the patience to put into a book everything I know about what goes on in the film world from the smallest pieces of offal to the Oscar Awards, it would be such an overflowing dust-bin load that would make the novels of Sagan and others which take the counterpane from the bed seem very moral and discreet indeed.

'The crowd film-agent I went to first of all, although he was always so busy, was of a very kind disposition, darting in and out of his inner office and swivelling his eyes around and calling to those he wanted to give them their immediate assignments and make more room in his office. Nobody took any notice of me. Those who already knew each other were all talking in loud voices and as soon as the agent appeared they would make a rush towards him and I would be pushed aside. Sometimes I never got beyond the stairs, the congestion upon them was so great, but at last one afternoon being the first to arrive, I was bold enough to waylay him in the vestibule as he returned after lunch. He regarded me keenly and asked me what I thought he could do for me. I beseeched him to spare me five minutes before the crowds would be filling his waiting-room again. He unlocked the outer door of his office and told me to follow him up the stairs.

'At last I found myself in his inner office. He sat at his desk and asked me a few interested questions. I told him of my famous papa who had been Nemo, whose revered name he knew immediately, and of how since he had been lost to me through the horrors of the concentration camp,

I had been cared for by strangers who were in distress themselves until finally I had become a cabaret dancer in a Berlin café amongst the rubbles and stones of bombed buildings until I received my injuries because of my much overdrunk male support failing to balance me. I told him of the gallant young doctor who had witnessed the disaster, taken me under his care in the American Military Hospital, and how in the shortest time I became his bride, and then, almost immediately and most tragically, his widow. In a few moments of great urgency I poured out all there was to tell.

'The agent listened to me with sympathy, and then, as the five minutes interview was up and we could hear the voices of the crowd artistes filling up the waiting-room outside, he wrote me out the card I would have to present at the studios the next day.'

18

'CONSIDER me this afternoon as a long disc record that must play on. If I were to stop it midway it would be as if there were some pages missing from the book which the B.B.C.'s so genial and pleasant Eamonn Andrews would read from before he handed it finally to the person whose life history had been followed and chronicled within its covers. There are links which lead from one passage to another, as the different movements in a musical composition are all part of the whole. Looking back, as I am doing now, it becomes apparent that each one, however insignificant it may seem, is a link in the construction which has already been planned. Infinitesimal atoms as we all are, none of us are so diminutive as not to be important to God. The faultlessness of tiniest detail as it is being discovered by men in this space age where mathematics and calculation are assurances that there is a supreme Being who works in this manner and establishes with all certainty this link with the Truth.

'My experience at the Ace Film Studios at Elstree was one of these tiny links, purposeless and very difficult and wearisome though it seemed, leading to nowhere except that tedious waiting around all day amongst the crowd until the assistant-producer assembled us to take up our positions. I was also finding it was very expensive. I had to make a spending out of the money in the bank to buy myself the smart clothes which an extra is expected to provide for day and evening wear. Period costumes or fancy dresses only came out of the studio wardrobe. My earnings were not sufficient to put back what I had spent.

'None of those hundreds of resigned persons who find work in the crowd have any false hopes or illusions that they will be lifted out of it by a talent-spotter. The talent scouts are not spotting in any such directions, not in those times or in these days when the procedure is exactly the same and all in a tabulated precise card-indexed form. If it were conducted in any other manner it would be impossible. The wastage of valuable time which swallows vast sums of money is more prevalent in the film industry than any other trade, and a great proportion of this can be ascribed very often to the unpredictable behaviour of the principals themselves whose inflated box-office values has made them go Hollywood, while others remain staunch troupers to the end, who would give their lives even if sickness deters them, rather than impede a production once it has commenced. Of such are names not yet forgotten on the roll of honour as glorious as if they had fallen in battle though they were before my day, Valentino in the full blaze of his fame, and the Englishman, Jameson Thomas, who faded out in great poverty of consumption in an American hospital. And in more recent times, Gary Cooper who died in brave character to the last, Errol Flynn who joked more than he drank and whose wicked, wicked life was a part-fabrication of the publicity agents who very often manufacture or exaggerate the reputations in a swashbuckling personality like his. His many scandalous affairs and pursuits of the young girls he invited to come sailing with him on his yacht were, I have full reason to know, a gross exaggeration. He enjoyed to be a playboy very often, but he could do many other things besides play and he was no stealing fox amongst the chickens. A much older woman, pasée and tired, would receive a pressing invitation from him to recuperate upon a pleasure cruise and upon her he would bestow, the same courtier-like attention and flowery compliments he would lavish upon the youngest. It was his exhuberant overflowing nature and desire to give pleasure all round. I have been a guest on Erroll's yacht and like to remember his generous and expanding nature and everything that was so fine in him. How he would chuckle and make a joke about it when his wicked life was published in a Sunday newspaper.

'You may well wonder how is it that these famous names ever come to be blazoned.

'Now that I have been mentioning Erroll as one, this is his history which in Hollywood is known.

'In England, hanging about on the sets, though full of joy of life and ready for anything, his lively Irish temperament refusing to be made miserable, the weather-cock of his uncertain fortunes suddenly veered round. Due to a close resemblance he was engaged by a Hollywood motion picture company as stand-in for Robert Donat, the so deservedly loved star in the rôle of Captain Blood, that super-film of a romantic pirate from the novel by Rafael Sabatani.

'During Captain Blood, Donat was forced to give up and Erroll Flynn was called upon to fill his place.

'From the moment of the showing of that film Erroll Flynn became a Name to be lit up in Neon by the bursting personality he created for himself which none could imitate, yet if the weather-cock had not changed its course, he might still have been gaily accepting more pieces of offal from the butcher's shop and never heard of!

'Then, how, you may wonder, did the changing wind blow the weather-cock to point in my direction? By just such a chance, most unexpected and so sudden that my first sensation was as if I had been pitched high up in one of those swing boats on a fairground. I could not have contrived anything of the kind for myself.

'At last I had been given my first bit-part in a crowd scene. That is I had two lines to speak which would mean four guineas instead of two in my pay-envelope, but that was not the reason I was so delighted. It was because the scene was a beer garden in Austria with small tables set out beneath the flowering cherry trees and lilacs all around in full bloom. I do not suppose there is any need to describe it to you. In your travels you may have seen it all. The air of verisimilitude was enchanting because the trees themselves were real and growing, brought straight from a near-by orchard, embedded in their own soil. In the distance, depicted by the scenic artist there were the pine trees and forests and the mountains with little rosy clouds floating on top.

'I was dressed in the costume of a peasant girl with a high stand-up head-dress of stiffened lace with floating ribbons, embroidered muslin blouse, black velvet laced-up bodice and full flared skirt. My bit-part was to bring forth flagons of lager for the students to drink while they sang and joked in roisterous mood. My spoken lines in German were delivered when one of the students, making a pass at me, pulled me on to his knee and my response was to turn from laughter to indignation, to struggle and protest.

'It was such a very easy little bit-part to portray and I was so happy to be wearing that *madchen* costume in a setting that was so dear and familiar to me that I was almost dancing between the tables forgetting that it was only a studio scene, which when it was over would be dismantled and put away, the hired cherry and lilac trees returned to the orchard which had supplied them and the hired extras to their so ordinary homes. None of them had seen and loved Austria as I had with all the happiest memories of my childhood and the friendly family brother-and-sister atmosphere of the circus without rivalries and conceits, with jolly greetings between the highest trapeze artiste and star performers to the tent workers, hammer-gang, seat men and tent-troupers, where there was *cameraderie* amongst all and not one was too great in his own eyes to notice the undistinguished or small. The spirit of the circus is that all those who are on or in the show are with it.

'Amongst variety folk this kind of friendliness also prevails, but not so, or very seldom, amongst the heavy names in the films or in the theatre world where the jealousies and petty rivalries are so acute and the fear of losing their own positions makes them wish to tighten the ring to keep others out and themselves apart.

'Your own sweet Queen, the Queen Mother, and all of the Royal Family can walk amongst the crowds and smile and mingle without pride or haughtiness or loss of dignity. Neither is their charming cordiality a pretence. It is out of their own true and genuine feelings and cannot be simulated.

'But the Kings and Queens and Knights and Ladies of the films and the stage erect a barrier of superiority and disdain between themselves and the insignificant. They do not even see them, much less notice them. They pass them by as if they were not there. Their crowns and their jewels and decorations are all as false as their sense of values.

'Halt me! I am becoming over-worded.

'Back to the Austrian beer-garden set on the Ace Film Company studio floor.

'Occasionally there would be, not the talent scouts whose attentions would be upon the inferior repertory companies for their type-castings, and this method of selection is still the same, but a few favoured important visitors invited by someone on the directorate to make a tour of the studios to witness a scene as it was going on. Otherwise "No Admittance" in large black forbidding letters and the entrance gates more difficult to pass through than if the studios were Buckingham Palace or the White House. On this morning as we in the beer-garden crowd were waiting for the word to commence on the "take", there was a whisper passed around that meant nothing to me because at that time I had little knowledge of the names of the foremost British playwrights, I was so ignorant.

'The whispered name was that of Guy Copthorn, the author of many successful plays, the latest of which was just about to be transferred to America, and he was seated in the chair next to the producer!'

19

THE pretty blonde florist's sales girl greeted Gerard familiarly as she twisted across the floor-space between counter and shop window on stiletto-heeled, winkle-picker Italian-made shoes.

'Lilacs, the same as usual? It's been lilacs for the past ten days! Well, the season for them won't be lasting for ever. Another fortnight and they'll be over. I've kept them on order especially for you and her. What kind of flowers will you be wanting next when the lilacs have given out? Carnations, roses, lilies, sweet peas? There's plenty of choice. How would you like to be interviewing me for the Telly for a change? If I win the next first prize in the Twist competition I'll be in the running for a Miss Celebrity. I'm learning to play the guitar, too, and to sing while I'm twisting. I'll let you know when I'm ready. I might get you twisting. That would be a change, wouldn't it? Here's your lilacs. The price has gone up, but I daresay you think she's worth it. Who is she?'

Gerard accepted the pert badinage with good humour but did not satisfy her curiosity. He paid for the lilacs and went forth to keep his appointment with Frieda. Without any reminder from the salesgirl he was deeply conscious of the fact that by the time the lilacs had ceased to bloom, those hours spent in her company which he had come to look upon as infinitely precious, would be over. What after?

In this real life enactment of her passing his way could it all end on as abrupt and inconclusive a note as so many of the plays on television? Was the meaning of such a brief encounter merely that he, as chronicler of this her authentic personal narrative, would have set his hand to a tribute as poignant and final as the French agnostic Renan's exalted dedication of his life's work on the Isle of Patmos to the memory of his beloved sister, Henriette?

Frieda rejoiced as soon as he presented her with the fresh lilacs.

'How bounteous you are to me in your continuous gifts of my favourite flowers, and not only in the flowers you bring, but in the time you give to me, when your days must be so full of appointments in so many directions. How empty they would have been for me if our meeting had not occurred and I had been in one of my withdrawn female hermit-crab moods when I cannot bear to see anyone and have closed myself up in my shell. I shall never forget you, dear friend. Make sure of that. Your name is already inscribed with the date of our meeting in my little red notebook of the people I shall never forget because I do not want to forget. And perhaps you will always think of me when the lilac seasons are here and you smell their sweet delicate scent? I hope so. Between us, I think, I feel, I sense there must be an invisible bond. When I woke up this morning there was the sunshine streaming on my face and my first thought was that you would be here in the afternoon, and I felt refreshed although I had not had a very good night. Now, first of all, let me attend to these flower-children. I cannot bear to see flowers out of water, or in water that has not been changed. I seem to hear them crying so softly and pitifully that they are thirsty for the water that is their life. The noblest of the elements is water. It cleans and it refreshes. It sparkles and it sings when it comes out of the springs from behind the deep bosoms of Mother Earth and bubbles into the streams to join the river and the sea!'

'You said a line of poetry!'

'Did I? You have not yet shown me any of the poems which you told me you are impelled to write when the spirit is upon you, but you are to reserved to let me see them. There! Drink, my little ones!'

Frieda had filled the flower-vases and arranged the lilacs. Almost maternal was the caress in her expression as she stepped back to admire them.

'You love children, don't you?' Gerard could not help remarking.

'Oh, yes, with all of me, but I never had a child, a baby of my own to cuddle. Perhaps it is best that the cradle under my heart was never filled. A mother can love too much and ruin the greatest responsibility she was given in trust. My love today extends most of all to the little children and orphans of the homeless and refugees. I can hear them crying sometimes like the untended flowers, but what can I do? When I see these poor mites sometimes pictured in the newspapers with their attenuated little bodies held up in the arms of some kind nurse or good nun with that look of child-wonder that has something of heaven in it still in their eyes, my affection goes out to each single one. Are you fond of children as well, Gerard? I am sure you must be. Then you should not leave it too long before you are married and have a family of your own. And if one of them is a little girl and I am still around somewhere in this world, I would like to be her god-mother and for her to be called Frieda after me.'

'Frieda—'

'Ah! Don't finish! I have an idea of what you might be

114

going to say. And if I allowed you to say it, my inclination to be gathered into your arms might become too strong. Schubert composed an unfinished symphony. It was not in the stars that he was able to complete it down here, but still it was a most beautiful piece of music. So it could be a symphony between two persons in our state who are melodiously attuned, and who shall say how it will be for us? Now, shall I resume my history for you where I broke it off when I was given that *madchen* bit-part at the Ace Film Studios at Elstree?

'Though I was not aware of it then, as the clapper-boy registered the "take" was over with his noisy pieces of numbered wood, that sound held a significance for me indicative of another move which would change the scene so quickly that there would be no time to waver or hesitate.

'The producer then called a temporary halt, and all of us in that cherry orchard scene were disbanding to go upstairs to the dressing rooms to change out of our picturesque costumes when the assistant-producer came swiftly after me and said that the producer wished to speak to me. He was a nice young man with a pleasant manner and so painstaking in assembling us all in our various positions and explaining what we were required to do. An assistant producer's job is not an enviable one, but he can learn much from it that will lead to promotion so that one day he may even come to direct a picture himself. He is what I would describe as an odd-job man for the producer. In a huge production such as "Antony and Cleopatra" or "King of Kings" there would be five or six or more to handle the mob-scenes. A sheep-herder is one of the studio names he is given. All his attention must go into the smallest details from the correct setting of a dinner-table with the cutlery, glasses, flower-arrangements, foods or drinks made out of cold tea poured ready into decanters or bottles with spirituous liquor labels, and all other kinds of properties needed. It must be a very exacting position, especially when the producer is of an explosive impatient disposition as so many of them are. I do not blame the producers either for their irascibility. The responsibility and the heavy load upon their shoulders of the so many millions or thousands that are being expended is enormous, and the money-men who have supplied it have one consideration only, which is that time should not be wasted and the tide of dollars flow back to them in a swollen stream. And yet it is a curious contradiction that in these vast productions there is nothing so much wasted as time which cannot be put back any more than the tide when it recedes.

'I was nervous that the assistant director had halted me because I was afraid I had done something that had displeased the producer. Had I been over drawing attention to myself in my exuberance as I danced between the tables under the cherry trees, forgetting in my delight that the lovely familar Austrian scene was an imitation? For an extra bit-part player to obtrude in such a way is foolish and deserves to be rebuked.

'The young fellow reassured me.

' "It's nothing to be scared about. This might be a lucky break for you. I heard what they were saying. Guy Copthorn is interested in you. He thinks you are a potential."

'So I found myself introduced in a most affable, friendly, manner by the producer to the famous playwright whom I did not then recognize as a play-daddy. Strange though it may seem, in my growing out of childhood and young girl life among the war-blasted ruins when I was sheltering amonst the homeless and unfortunates in Berlin, it was they who succoured and protected me so that I was as safe from molestation as if I had been cared for in a convent. The kindness of human beings towards each other, and to the very young and the very old, the weak and the helpless in times of stress, is always a complete proof to me of the existence of the benign Love which surrounds everyone of us and against which even the atom bomb and every other device of destruction is powerless.

'Over this interlude I prefer not to linger. It did not do me any harm, and the contract which was offered to me to play a small part as a German maid-servant in the American production on Broadway of Guy Copthorn's play to open in a fortnight, filled me with elation.

'As you must know Guy Copthorn died two years ago, and it is not charitable to speak unkindly of the dead. I have heard he was enormously rich, very old, very tired and very lonely, but he has left some plays which will continue to shed lustre on his fame, and strangely enough, for those who knew him, there was no corruption in them.'

20

FRIEDA was anxious to maintain the continuity of her life-story to date, especially now that there were ten days only remaining for her to unfold it. Her thoughts, once she was in the flow of expressing herself in words, ran swiftly ahead of her and she found it a little difficult to stick to the chronological order of events while she was revealing herself so naturally and spontaneously to this one person who seemed to understand her so well in so short a time.

This afternoon, before she began to talk, Gerard removed a folder from his portfolio containing the typewritten script of all he had set down so far. He gave it to her.

'This is your life,' he said. 'Look over it at your leisure. I would like to have your full approval of everything I have written about you. If there is anything you would like left out I would far rather you told me. My intention is that all of it should be entirely factual and non-controversial and to avoid any suggestion of the enigmatic capricious legend your public seems to have built around you as one of its idols, exceeding the legend of Garbo.'

'Ach! The public!' The Germanic pronunciation of her interjection carried a touch of impatience with it. 'The public has a disposition to regard itself as the Gods of Olympus where its favourites are concerned. It seems to consider that our homes and our lives should be in a glass house for everything that happens to be seen and known and gossiped about. Whether it be the tenderness of lovers, the quarrels and the tempests and the jealousies and controversies between those who have married and not had time to adjust themselves which might be averted if they were allowed to die down as the bonfires when the wind ceases to blow; to sit in judgment, to frown, mock or laugh, flatter and adulate or turn its thumbs up or down. I made my resolution as soon as I became known, that my privacy and my home life when I had a home, must not be invaded. It is my own. I am the willing servant of the public and grateful for the recognition it has given me when I came before it. I wish and strive to give of my utmost, all of me even if it is only to make gay the sad, to send them away with something more than the price of the seat they have paid for. It is a form of immediate communication and an interchange of a most subtle rewarding nature that only show-people know because it happens on the instant, not when an interval of time has elasped as when a writer has a book published, or an artist exhibits his pictures. It is at the conclusion of a performance when the audience has left and gone home that the curtain should remain lowered until the next show as it is in the theatre. The audience does not wish to go behind and watch the artists disrobe and remove their grease-paints. It prefers to keep its illusions of the painted scenes and the persons in the play. I have refused to be obstructed and enslaved because I am a favourite. I have been accused of moodiness, but that is not true. Never in all my career have I failed my producer to turn up or to plead I am sick, but I must have my privacy. Do you blame me?'

'Far from it. I think you are entirely right, and though

I am a newspaper-man myself I would be inclined to put the blame on the gutter-press and not the public itself. The public is only a led horse.'

Frieda was turning over the pages of typescript with her slender fingers, the shell-pink nails neatly trimmed and shaped, not sharply elongated or painted in the crimson shades which, like most men, he disliked to see. How pale, almost to transparency were her small hands! The extreme fragility of her physical structure as well as her colouring which was devoid of all beautician's artifices made apparent the delicacy of a constitution which had been undermined through the stresses of war conditions in those waif-childhood days; and ever since her invincible spirit had refused to be daunted, or even to nurse her weakness when nervous exhaustion caused by the exactingly long hours under the arc lights of the film studios or the dusty stuffiness of stage rehearsals in the darkened theatre, accelerated the dread malady for which an indefinable period of rest had been urged by her medical advisers. The film magnates had early recognized and exploited the sex-appeal of this amazingly versatile Continental artist, but it was in the theatre that she was able to display the genius that illuminated her art.

The carefully set out script evidently pleased her. She turned back to the first page.

'I will consider all of this very carefully before I give it back to you. Thank you for bringing it to me. Thank you for wishing to make me the subject of your writing. I do not consider that I am so important a person as to have a book written concerning me. I know that what you write will be the last pronouncement, and it is an honour. Here in the foreword which I like so much, it is so tenderly expressed, I see you have described me as I seem to you, a portrait in words in the softest pastels, as if you had put it out in the dew to be washed for the colours to merge. Do I seem as beautiful as that to you?'

'So beautiful that I wish I could handle a brush as well as a pen. Words are an insufficient medium by themselves to convey you as I see you.'

'Angonini made a sketch of me in pastels when I was filming in Rome last year. His intention was for it to be the study for a full-sized portrait in oils, but I had no time to spare even for that one sitting. When I had been in his studio for less than half-an-hour the film tyrants discovered where I had gone and came suddenly to fetch me. The new arrangements were I must pack up immediately because it had been decided suddenly to transfer the location for the rest of the shooting to Malaga, in Spain. So Angonini made me a graceful present of the unfinished sketch. If you would care to have it reproduced for your book or to keep for yourself I will send it to you when I get back. It is a gem although it is incomplete and he did not have time to draw my feet!' She flicked back to the last page.

'How conscientious you are in your method of work! Chapter nineteen up to here, and in the very same words as I was speaking them! Is it possible you have one of those cunning pocket-recorders hidden in your jacket that you are so accurate, but if I thought so it would dry me.'

'Nothing of that kind, I assure you. It merely means that my mind is a piece of blotting paper.'

'My imperfect English, I notice, you have left it exactly as I twist it sometimes. Would it not be wiser to correct it? Is it not possible one of your readers might not think it was careless writing?'

'It is as fascinatingly endearing as your accent. I wouldn't wish to correct a single word of it, not even when you informed me the other day you had been to Fish-Mackeries to buy some smoked salmon!'

'Ah! That was an extra stupid one. Macfisheries, of course. I saw you smile. Then I realized at once it was the cart in front of the horse after the word had jumped out and no wonder you were amused. Fill up your pipe, my dear Gerard. I like to see the short stem of it between your lips and the little dent in your tooth it rests on while the bowl of it bobs about like a small boat as you puff. You have a peaceful effect on me, and when you have left I like the fragrant peaty heather-mixture smell that is left behind which mingles with my lilacs but does not overpower them. I can still feel your presence after you have gone. We are very much attuned, you and I. Your friendship is like a sheltering tree to me after the scorching sun of so much movement and publicity. I am so grateful for the shade! I would like to stay beneath it like the weary traveller in a desert of sand who has come a long way.'

'Frieda, my dearest! Couldn't you consider the possibility of giving it all up and allowing someone who cares for you to look after you? My greatest reward would be to see you recuperate and grow stronger, to take you away to a lovely little home far from cities and pavements, to give you a horse to ride, and all the joys and delights of the countryside.'

'So kind of you! If I was somebody else, not myself, but as it is, I have to continue. It is not the acclamation and the popularity alone that pulls me in another direction, although I would not be speaking the truth if I did not admit that when there are huge crowds recognizing me such as on the day I was presented with my Oscar, throwing confetti and paper streamers and flowers out of balconies and in the streets pressing forward to see me, calling "Frieda! Frieda!

Frieda!" Then I admit I experienced the sensation of what a royal personage must feel who is loved by the multitude. I could feel the love of the multitudes warming me like the heat for a brazier. Neither is it the thought of money, although I have never kept it to breed like some do. I would as soon breed snails if they had gold shells. I dislike snails. They are slimy. It is the blood of my dear papa in my veins, the job where you work that will not allow me to stop. Can you think of yourself leaving Fleet Street, where you work, behind you or throwing away your precious pen? What would you feel like if it was not there, clipped in your breast coat pocket, filled and ready to be used? The working journalist, the newspaper proprietor with his take-overs and chains of publications whose commencement was selling newspapers in the streets, he cannot stop until his clock stops. He has wound himself up and set himself in motion. He revolves with his printing presses and so with you and me. While we remain in the workshop of the world it must be so. We cannot change ourselves if we are not all planted in the vegetable plot of existence. I would rather be devoured by my own energies than by the slugs and caterpillars! Now, are you ready for me to keep the ball rolling, to continue with your next chapter after I have been given the contract to appear in New York in Guy Copthorn's new play?'

21

FRIEDA resumed:

'That experience which transferred me to a luxury-liner with my second-class passage paid to New York in company of seven others, was to be a very brief one after all, for the reason that although Mr. Copthorn's play had been a success, with a considerable run before that in London, it was not received well in New York and was, therefore, withdrawn after three weeks only. Its tempo was too slow for American audiences, and the subject, which was of a deeply metaphysical nature concerning two men whose identities were changed through the death of one, did not capture their imagination. The Americans are very down to earth. Tenessee Williams and Arthur Miller express what they feel. My own small part in it had no acting significance whatever. All I had to do was to make a few utterances in German and to appear as a schoolgirl in a gym-slip. I was not so over-much disappointed over this because I was so full of rejoicing that the liner was taking me overseas to Bill's country. I was quite poor by this time, as the background-girl fashionable frocks I had to provide for myself when I was an extra at the Elstree studios had cut a big hole in my money, but I was so thankful to have proceeded out of the butcher's shop. I felt that I was on my way to somewhere. Because of my Bill I already had an affectionate feeling for all Americans before I came to be amongst them or to know them as I do today, and it is how I feel at the present time after so many years of citizenship. The affectionate feeling has deepened and I have great gratitude for the recognition that has been given to me.

'I suppose it is because compared with the other nations it is such a young country that the Americans are so natural, so expansive, so friendly and young in heart. You may not agree with me. I do not know your opinions of the American disposition. There is no harshness in the American nature, which is largely conveyed by the quickness of its utterance and its agility of mind in making swift decisions; but its nature is beneficent and sincere. If America in the future makes any big mistakes as a nation, it will not be through greed for gain, but out of the indomitable spirit of the young man in the poems of Longfellow to plant his banner with the strange Excelsior device as he climbs higher and higher up the mountain until he has reached the summit. That is how I think of President Kennedy. There is no guile in him, and in his single-hearted zest, which is without personal conceits or ambitious self-aggrandisement, for he has no need of such, and with his firm religious faith and convictions, he may lead this distressed world out of the wilderness. America does not want war. That is the reason why America has always held back until the decision was inevitable. I did not mean to make a political speech.

'Back to my story.

'Guy Copthorn did not mingle with his company of players on the way out. He remained aloof. He was travelling first-class, of course, amongst the V.I.P's, a small, completely bald-headed, insignificant man with the strutting gait of a bantam rooster, with a high-pitched voice so that one would not be very surprised to hear him crow. I had no idea when I was first invited to his agent's office to sign the contract to be in his play that he was wearing the red comb for me. He had not been present at that time and I had not seen him to speak to personally since the day we had embarked and he had shaken hands with us all and wished us a pleasant voyage. The red comb did not appear until the last evening of the voyage after dinner, when I received a scribbled note brought by one of the stewards, requesting me to come to his state room as he had been making certain alterations to my exits and entrances which he would like to give to me to carry through on my own script as it would save time at rehearsals.

'As the young steward, who had a cheeky demeanour, was waiting to conduct me to the first-class regions, I went with him without hesitation and was escorted to the luxurious state-room of a V.I.P. Knocking at the door of an adjoining compartment, he announced me, and as he was leaving the state-room he smirked and winked and made the murmured remark that I was too pretty for a piece of alligator's bait. What rudeness! Did he think because he was a first-class steward he could speak with such disrespect to a second-class passenger! I tossed my head and retorted "*Quatch!*" to him, which in colloquial German is a forceful term meaning "Shut up!"

'Standing there, I took a swift impressed note of this commodious state-room which only such a successful play-wright as Mr. Copthorn could afford to pay for. In my eyes it had a truly regal appearance furnished with deep-seated armchairs, a most luxurious fixed bed instead of the bunk with two bunks in it one above the other as in the cramped second-class cabin which I shared with another girl in the company, small tables, and a desk at which Mr. Copthorn had evidently been writing, for it was scattered with many sheets of manuscript covered with handwriting. On one of

126

the small occasional tables was a huge be-ribboned pre-sentation box of Black Magic chocolates that apparently, he must have bought especially for this occasion which seemed very gracious of him.

'When in the next moment he entered I was taken aback by his unconventional appearance. As dinner-service in the upper deck saloon was not long over and I had seen many of the passengers strolling about the deck in their correct evening dress, it seemed surprising that in so short an in-terval he should have changed from his dinner-jacket to blue silk pyjamas and brocade dressing-gown of a most re-splendent Oriental pattern. Still, as it was a very warm evening perhaps he preferred to feel more cool and com-fortable and ready to retire early as soon as he had con-cluded his interview with me. I was not nervous. His manner of greeting was so urbane and agreeable.

The audacious young steward then re-entered with the coffee equipage, wineglasses and a variety of liqueurs in small coloured bottles. After pouring the coffee and Mr. Copthorn had selected a very special brand of cigar for himself, he drew the curtains over the portholes, switched off the bowl-shaped centre light leaving only the shaded lights, and discreetly withdrew with a sidelong glance under his eyes at me. Then I did not feel quite so com-fortable as before although I was still unprepared for the *dénouement*.

'At first Mr. Copthorn's pleasantly expanding manner was reassuring, as lifting the artistic picture-lid from the magnificent box of chocolates he offered it to me, saying "Sweets for a sweetie," and telling me to make my choice, he selected for me a liqueur called *crême de vanille* which would blend well with the delicious sweets. It had a warm, sweet flavour and was very pleasant.

'Quite naturally I felt agreeably complimented that he should take the trouble to wish to entertain me in this way, considering that my part was of the smallest importance of all the seven persons in the cast of his play. The shaded lights and the switched-off centre light should have prepared me, I daresay, but I was very naïve in those days.

'He did not seem to be in a hurry to discuss the alterations to begin with, but proceeded to tell me about the next play he had already commenced to write, in which he said there might be a considerable rôle for me. He would like to develop and build around me as he came to know me better, which was essential in creating a character to be what he described as a glove-part.

'He said that I was at the exact right tender age to be moulded and shaped by a mature, experienced old hand like himself, whose principal interest besides his literary work was to promote and encourage the talents of youth. I did not disbelieve him. He seemed so genuine, and I suppose I was a little dazzled in that short while to find myself the object of such benevolence as expressed by one of his fame and distinction. He drew his chair close beside me, his knees touching mine, and himself wrote in my copy of the play-script the few minor changes which were of so trifling a nature that it made me think it was even more kind of him to take the trouble to send for me and inform me of them with such a sociable intent.

'I was totally unprepared for the swift disillusionment which followed when, almost as if he was arranging a different stage effect, Mr. Copthorn got up and very deliberately switched off the various shaded lights, leaving two only, one of which shed its rosy beam upon the gigantic box of Black Magic chocolates, and the other a dimmed amber light over the bed with its un-masculine drapings. He came and stood beside me. The burning of his hot hands as he pressed them over my shoulders penetrated through the thin cotton summer frock I was wearing, and his hot breath scorched the back of my bare neck as, standing behind me, he bent over me, and it was only then the position was made clear to me that the cheeky young steward's allusion to an alligator was not incorrect.

'On a very few occasions I have a spasmodic temper which I have learned to control now that I am so much older. This egg-headed, oldening man, famous and important though he was – how dare he! So I reacted furiously and in one indignant sweep I tossed those many chocolates in their box right up in the air, scattering them all over the state-room, and one of them with a soft creamy centre broke upon his cheek and into his eye, spattering it like a custard-pie.

'Here ended the carefully planned seduction scene in a most high comedy manner. I rushed out of the V.I.P. state-room at full speed, down to the lower deck and into my second-class cabin, where I soon cooled down and laughed, seeing the funny side, when I recounted the incident to the girl I shared it with. Thereafter I became a much wiser girl, firm in my resolve that whatever trials might be ahead of me I would achieve my goal in the same courageous spirit that had inspired my beloved papa both in the circus ring, where he so often tumbled and bruised himself though he picked himself up and joked and laughed all the more to cover the hurts and make people laugh, and in the cruel concentration camp where he was tortured. It was in his unbreakable spirit.

'So would I be my father's proud daughter and keep flying aloft the unbought flag of my womanhood.'

22

GERARD apologized for the not-so-fresh quality of the lilacs he brought for Frieda on his next visit.

'I almost hesitated to bring these. You can see the frost has nipped them a bit. The girl in the florist's shop didn't want to sell them to me. At this time of the year one expects to have finished with wintry weather. It certainly has been one of the worst on record, with ice, snow, floods, gales and all the rest.'

'Ah! Your unconstant climate! I am fond of England, and I think she is only spoken of as perfidious because of her so changeable seasons. The lilacs for me always! You were quite right to bring them, even though the edges have curled and their colour has the tinge that says they are feeling sickly and drooping, in the stage before they must fade and disappear. But what a message they leave behind that there will come another springtime and they will be in flower again! How long this year the Spring is in delaying its delightful appearance! If only I could have stayed a little longer until June and taken a brief rest in the loveliest month of the year, deep down somewhere in the heart of the country where the greenness of England is so superb. . . . But never mind, perhaps if I do not get nipped by the killer-frost like these tender flowers I will be returning some time. Do not think I am altogether resigned not to see you again, but if it is not to be, the cherishment of our friendship will remain evergreen even when this book of my re-collections you are near to completing has reached the final chapter, whichever way you end it. You have pre-sented me in a highly realistic manner. As I was reading the typescript you left for me I could almost hear my own self speaking. Chapter Twenty-two now! I am ready if you are.'

'Frieda, if you talked sheer rubbish, which you never do, I should be content to listen just to the sound of your voice!'

'Thank you, dear. Guy Copthorn does not make a per-sonal second appearance into this one. Except at rehearsals, I never saw him any more, but put this on record – that when that brief three weeks run of his play was over I received a registered package containing a jeweller's case. Inside it was one beautiful pearl set as a pendant with his visiting card on which he had written the words:
"For a good little girl, with best wishes from a hardened old sinner. Virtue is a pearl of great price."
So, you see, in spite of my angry behaviour in scattering those chocolates, he had not felt resentful against me after all. It was a generous and kind gesture, and I wrote, care of his agent in London, to thank him and tell him that I was very proud to accept that lovely pearl. It is amongst my few treasures I would not wish to sell or care to lose, otherwise jewellery does not appeal very much to me.

'So now what was I to do with very little money left except the price of my second-class fare back to England which was in my last pay-envelope handed to me with my salary by the business manager on that last Friday when the play ended? The rest of the disappointed company of players were all returning to London, with a lot of grum-bling amongst them, but I felt, if possible, now I was in Bill's country I would prefer to remain there. As I was an

American citizen by marriage there would be few difficulties about that, and I would not need to apply for a permit to be earning dollars. I decided I would proceed to Hollywood and begin once more as an extra.

'The cheapest way would be to travel there by Transcontinental Greyhound Coach Line from New York to Los Angeles, and it would enable me to see the country in a more leisurely way than in aeroplane or rushing train. The three-day journey was most enjoyable, and the passengers so friendly and ready to advise where I should go to find not too expensive accommodation. Most of them were business men or women, and several, like myself, were hoping to find employment in the studios which at that time were busy enough, for these were still the days when Hollywood was flourishing and Rome and Spain were not being so much frequented by the film units.

'Once again I struck a bad patch. Almost immediately I was made very ill through being over-drenched in a watery scene where I was an extra, which had to be repeated for re-takes with no opportunity to dry myself. Rheumatic fever was the complaint, and I was in hospital for three weeks, emerging in a very poor condition because now all my money had gone to pay the medical expenses which in the United States are not free, and it is a calamity to fall ill if one has no friends or relatives to care for one. One has to pay or fall by the way.

'I was not strong enough to return to the studios for more work. Naturally in my loneliness and desperation the thought of Bill's sister came into my mind. I still had the letter he had written to her concerning me and not had courage to post when that dreadful accident causing his death had intervened, but even so I felt shy and hesitant about making myself known to her, more especially now that I was in such a state of destitution. Yet I recalled how in speaking of her he had assured me I would be certain to love her, and she would love me.

'I summoned up my courage and made up my mind I would visit her and tell her all and ask her to lend me enough money to pay my landlady for my cheap apartment. Then as soon as I was strong enough and working again, I would repay her. It is a shameful thing, if one has the spirit of independence in one's nature, to come to it that one has to ask for money. I had never done it before, not even in those war days when I was existing amongst the stones and rubble in bombed-out Berlin. We shared our tribulations and discomforts, but no one begged or borrowed. To beg or borrow is not necessary when all are ready to give more than to receive. Why should this not be in peace as well as in war?

'The locality of her home was the select Bel Air residential district which is about four miles from Hollywood; and going there by bus, and finding my way after being given directions by the helpful conductor, I came to a most gracious dwelling made of pine logs, with a verandah around it, set well back from the roadway in a most beautiful garden. On the wooden gate was carved the name which so truly describes it – "Dream Cottage." Standing there and seeing it for the first time it was so like a dream that I would not have been surprised if I had woken up and found that was what it was.

'At the back there seemed to be a good deal more land where there were outbuildings and kennels with wire-netted runs in which a number of dogs of all sorts and sizes were barking and jumping about with eager expectancy as a girl in kennel-maid's overall and breeches let them out and they all proceeded to the woodlands stretching beyond.

133

'Then, from the house on to the verandah, came a small woman with smooth fair hair simply arranged in braids twisted round her head. She was wearing a cotton frock and carrying a bowl out of which she took handfuls of meal and scattered it as she uttered a bird-call. Immediately from a neary-by tree several white doves fluttered to gather up the grain, one perching itself upon her shoulder, completely tame.

'Then, noticing me standing hesitantly by the gate, she came down the verandah steps and down the path to me with such a friendly look on her open face for one who was a complete stranger that immediately my shyness commenced to melt away. She had blue eyes like Bill's, the same healthy colouring and smiling expression which radiated goodness. In feature, too, there was the resemblance which proclaimed her as his sister. I felt as if in spirit Bill might be standing beside her at that moment.

' "Would you care to come and sit in the garden for a little while?" she invited. "You look very tired. It's far too long a walk if you've come all the way from the Convent to see me. Sister Margaret knows I am always willing to pay the coach-fares from there to here. You are Marjorie from the Convent? I was expecting you some time today."

'I said I would be very glad indeed to come into her beautiful garden, and that I did wish to talk with her most urgently, but I was not the person she had been expecting. My name was Frieda, and I was not from the Convent.

' "Never mind about that, Frieda," she said, and taking my hand she led me through the gate. "If you need me, that's what I'm here for, to help and be a friend whoever you are. Tell me whatever you wish to tell me, my dear. Sit down here, don't hurry away." She had brought me to a swinging cushioned garden seat for two and sat beside me.

134

'The words tumbled out and I could not hold them back by leading up to it in a more gradual way.

' "I'm Bill's widow," I said. "He wrote you a letter which he never had time to finish or post before he died." I took it from my bag and handed it to her.

'She gave a little gasp, catching her breath. Restraining herself, she took the letter from its envelope and read it once hurriedly, and then again slowly, the four pages of it. Of course her emotion was very great.

'She turned to me, her eyes shining with tears, but there was gladness in them as well. She opened her arms.

' "Dear little sister! My home is your home from today. My beloved husband, Bunny, and your Bill would have wished it this way, I know." '

23

'Mrs. Nancy Dean! Bill's sister!

'Though there will be very little in it about me, I would prefer that you write it as a chapter all to itself to make it my garland of love, thankfulness, respect and admiration of the dearest and best woman I have ever known. She is still most actively plunged into the never ceasing circle of her beneficent activities, and for many, many more years I hope she will remain as energetic and tireless as she is at present, for all the tremendous good that she does and that it is now her life's work to be dedicated.

'Weave all this into your chronicle, if you please.

'She is known throughout the Bel Air district and beyond it for her care of anyone who may be sick or in need, distress or trouble of any kind, and her abounding ministrations of mercy and humanity, most particularly for the strays of this life from boy or girl misfits and delinquents to lost and homeless dogs. There is nothing she would not and does not do, exercising all her influence and patience to help the maladjusted or the unfortunate. The Little Mother of Dream Cottage is how she is spoken of and known, and that is what they call her, and when they answer her whatever she may say to them it is, "Yes, Little Mother," or "No, Little Mother," or "Good night or good morning, Little Mother," those two affectionate words. Especially is she all in all to the younger ones, some of whom have never known any kind of maternal solicitude until she dawned upon them and changed their whole world. You may not be able to believe that such a person exists or that the circumstances I shall relate are not exaggerated, but I can assure you that they are true.

'Soon after I had gone to live with her and she had told me the story of her life from the time of her first meeting with the brilliant young artist who became her husband, I came to know the astonishing diversity of the good deeds she performed, and the spiritual experience she had received which had thenceforward directed her along the path of her angelic ministrations through all the sixteen years of her widowhood.

'It was at some charitable garden fête that they had found themselves side by side, Nancy in charge of a fancy-goods stall and he presiding over a coconut-shy for the kiddies, and between whiles they held snatches of conversation and found they had an immediate interest and liking for each other. Taking a glance at the objects on her stall he noticed two silver rings lying side by side for sale on which Zodiac signs were engraved. Picking one up to look at it because he had a faint interest in astrology and had been reading it up in a manual he saw that it was the sign of Capricorn which was his birth month; and what was the sign on the next one? It was the sign of Virgo which happened to be *her* birth-month, an amusing, but strange coincidence. He laughed and joked as he told her that in a happy, successful marriage partnership the signs were that those two months were favourable, so why not each make the other a present of a lucky ring according to the stars, and this they did, slipping on the rings, merrily laughing but keeping them on. Nancy still wears her ring as the engagement ring over her wedding ring, because that is what happened. Two months later those two happy persons were married. It was a romance which lasted for all the years they were to be together and they grew together like young trees.

'It was not all the easy way for them from the beginning. Bunny (whose Christian name was Bernard, and Bunny was only her love-name for him) had a true talent and the wish and longing to fulfil himself as an artist, a painter of landscapes, of trees, mountains, waterfalls, anything to do with nature, untouched and beautiful in all her changing moods of skies, clouds, dawns and sunsets. Nature is the art of God was his credo. His actual job at the time they met had been one he very much disliked for it was unsuitable to one of his aspirations. He was head clerk in a down-town drug-store. All he had been able to train himself to up till then was to attend Art School night classes, and when on camping holidays he had been able to do his sketching out of doors. Nancy had a very little money that had been left to her by her parents, and because she loved anything to do with delicate objects and art and seeing how they might combine the two, so that he could take up his art study seriously as a career, she opened a small shop selling needle-work, artcraft, china and glass which she learned how to paint and decorate herself, and semi-precious jewellery, giving it the name of Studio Fifty-Nine, which was the street number of the premises. Very beautiful they must have made it, painting it within and without according to their mutual ideas, leaving window and wall-space where Bunny could also show and sell those of his sketches which he thought good enough to exhibit as he painted them. Now assisted by Nancy, he was a full-time art student, pro-gressing and assiduous, becoming more and more fulfilled

138

and happy when he reached the final stage and his work was accepted and hung in galleries as well as becoming press-noticed and highly praised. It must have been a most perfect and contented relationship continuing for those many years. His pictures were in demand and fetched good prices and her side of the business prospered also. Between them they were able to purchase the woodland site for the Dream Cottage, where he could also establish his own school for art students. So the Dream Cottage was eventually built, the small shop-business was sold, and when all was ready they installed themselves there in Bel Air.

'They had no children of their own though both adored them. It was the only form of completion that had been withheld from them and even so there were the children of neighbours for whom they gave parties and picnics to add to the merriness and gaiety.

'They were both still comparatively young with so many more years together ahead of them before life even reached its autumnal stage. Bunny was forty and she two years younger when, without any warning, certain grave symptoms of a distressful complaint manifested themselves, and it was found that he who had been so handsome and strong and never ill in his life before was suffering from Bright's disease, and that this malady was not likely to be curable in spite of all skill and treatment, and devoted care from Nancy. If he lived, the ultimate state could be total blindness, an affliction which for him would be unthinkable and tragic, never more to be able to paint and depict all the beauties of the glorious scenery he so adored and which, in his paintings, he had perpetuated for others as he had seen it. Only for Nancy's sake, who would have been his two eyes, would he have wished to live, but that was not ordained to happen. He still had his sight although the lights and colours were beginning to dim, when quite suddenly the end came and he received his call, answering it very peacefully with his devoted wife by his bedside, turning to her at the last with such a lovely smile on his handsome face and the words: "Give my love to everybody and for you – all." They had so many friends and everybody loved him, she told me, wherever they went.

'In the first early stage of bereavement she was stricken and desolate. All reason for her own continued existence alone seemed to be gone. How could she carry on without him? Where in God's universe was he now and was ultimate reunion with one so dearly loved but a wishful mirage set in the arid desert of grief?

'She then confided to me the ineffable manifestation which had reorganized her life for her, and set right the course she was to follow which would mean re-union with him who had his continued work to do on the other side as all have according to the Divine Order.

'Light-hearted acquaintances and well-meaning friends had done their best, trying, to use that useless expression, "Take her out of herself" by insisting that she should go with them to places of entertainment and bright spots. This proved quite useless because, returning afterwards to the Dream Cottage, the sense of loss was even greater. Her sorrow seemed beyond all healing. Its pangs grew more and more desperate until she could not even bring herself to meet other persons who were gay and light-hearted. There came a moment when her endurance broke. She had not even been able to induce temporary forgetfulness of her misery in sleep because the long hours of the night would pass and she would be weeping and sobbing her heart out shedding the tears she had been restraining all day. Neither was she able to eat sufficiently to sustain herself, although the faithful coloured woman-servant who had been with them since they had gone to Dream Cottage would be at endless pains to prepare food that would tempt her. One eats because one must to sustain life, but she did not wish to live any longer. There seemed no remedy for her grief.

'The doctor had prescribed sleeping tablets of the barbiturate variety. One at bed-time and another if sleep was still withheld adding the caution that she must not exceed the dose or become the slave of a habit. She had obeyed his instructions, but without relief. Sleep, as well as any kind of consolation, seemed to be withheld.

'One Sunday evening after the Church Service she had gone as usual to her husband's grave in the adjacent churchyard, there to place the flowers from the garden which they had planted together, standing for a long time in her alone-ness, looking down upon the simple headstone in the shape of an artist's palette she had that last week caused to be placed there with words that he had himself written graven upon it. "The words for my counterpane when I go. See to it please, my darling." These words: *Bury me lightly so that the small rain may reach my face and the fluttering of the butterfly may not escape my ears.* Such lovely words, implying that however far he had travelled through infinity it was not beyond the soft kisses of the raindrops or the fluttering of the butterfly's wings.

'The hole in the grave was covered up, but the chasm in her heart was too deep to be filled.

'The used and discarded envelope of his dear body was in that hole with, placed by herself within his folded artists hands, the paintbrushes he had used. The physical part of him was perished and from that filled-in hole over which the grass had commenced to grow there was no hint of direction for her who had been so attuned to him that she was rudderless in her frail cockleboat of being upon an ocean of such loneliness and despair that turning to leave her beloved's grave she had no wish for continuance.'

24

'I THINK you will understand that all I have said so far and have yet to tell you about this heaven-sent little woman, sister and friend to me from those first moments, is no sort of digression. If my circumstances had not been linked with her in such a fond and close manner, I am certain my life would not have taken the shape and pattern that it did. First, by her loving solicitude she re-charged me with the motive-power to be a success in show-business – nursing and reviving me with the same extra attention she gave to the most delicate plants in her garden as to those other misdirected or unfortunate or sadly in need of comfort human beings who came within the range of her goodness. I have never known anyone take so little thought for herself. I do not think for herself now she exists at all.

'What she has done, and continues to do, and in what manner she was given the revelation of what her mission was to be through a Divine dispensation is as true and miraculous as the vision of the little Saint Teresa. The experience which Nancy received was as wonderful and sustaining to her, and to me to whom she told it, that I have never since had the slightest doubt of the existence of the spiritual and the necessity for the linking with it as vital and pressing as oxygen which has to be breathed for our blood to circulate to sustain our physical life whilst we remain within our material envelope.

'So now to tell you of this experience which happened to her after she had returned from her husband's graveside with that empty space in her heart, and nothing else but doubts and darkness and another period of slowly dragging hours as dark as a wolf's mouth to be faced unless she took a double dose of the barbiturate pills which, if they succeeded in shortening the night would only open the shutters once again to a beauty-less day.

'She took four pills, she says, and the night walked on its black leaden feet until from downstairs she heard the old clock with its brass face chiming three o'clock of the before dawn-time when the pulse of the human heart ticks its slowest and lowest.

'The bottle containing the barbiturate pills was on her bedside table. Why not swallow all that remained of them? It was three-quarters full, enough to ensure the longest and last sleep.

'She switched on her bedside light, fully intending to make that ending. For what purpose was she continuing to live? None whatever. She had reached her decision. She poured water into a tumbler. To dissolve the pills and drain the draught at once would be quicker and then there could be no hesitation after she had swallowed it. She dropped them in one by one, crushing and stirring them with a spoon until they were altogether dissolved. Death in the glass! As simple and as easy as that. Deep sleep and so deep peace, the peace of nothingness.

'She raised the tumbler to her mouth, but before it had reached her lips – and here comes the wonder – it was firmly lifted out of her hand and her astonished eyes saw it slowly levitated across the room to the wash-basin where it tipped and emptied itself.

'The occurrence took place so quickly and so quietly,

144

without any spilling or smashing, but as if a powerful unseen hand was responsible for the levitation. More was to come. The bulb of the table-lamp went suddenly out, yet the room was not plunged into darkness. It was filled with the silvery golden light of the moon which was shining through the open uncurtained window. Bunny and she had never been in the habit of closing or curtaining their windows at night. Both loved to look upon the sky and to breathe the fresh air which brought the perfume of the flowers outside into the room. It is a fragrance which is of an even deeper and more concentrated essence from sunset onwards. As the birds sing in the evening so I would call this scent the evensong of the flowers.

'She got out of bed and leaned out of the window. As she did so she, whose heart had been so heavy, was astonished at the lightness of her body, which seemed to be entirely weightless and without substance as if she could have floated out of the window into the moon-illumined garden outside. However, she went downstairs in the ordinary way though her feet scarcely seemed to touch the stairs. Their pet cat, a Siamese of which Bunny had been most fond and to which he had given the Egyptian name of Nefertiti, came out of the kitchen and followed her into the garden making the peculiar low murmuring affectionate sounds it had used to when he called to her. And when on occasions he had been out sketching or away for some little while, the cat seemed to be aware of the moment when he would return before he appeared and would be waiting to greet him.

'None of this seemed strange to Nancy. She knew now she was being impelled to go outside and that more was to come.

'The garden was drenched in silver and gold. The

flowers had a luminosity of their own and from everywhere so that it seemed to be proceeding from the flowers themselves, there stole on the ear, the soft and harmonic chanting of pure voices to the muted tones of an organ such as one might hear standing outside a cathedral, and it was followed by a religious hush of the kind that precedes the moment of pause before a consecration.

'Nancy was on the lawn in the centre of the garden, waiting. Each second was pregnant with meaning, of potency and quickening operative power, dynamic and wholly beneficent.

'Breaking the hush from without, from close by came the sharp bark of a dog. She knew that particular challenging bark, which was quite unmistakable, came from Timber, the wolfhound belonging to a neighbour, which sometimes forced an entrance through any available gap, and naughtily chased and terrified Nefertiti, if she happened to be in the garden, when she would seek refuge in the nearest tree and at a safe height she would defy and spit at him. They were declared enemies and Timber was a nuisance when he broke free from his own premises.

'Nefertiti heard the barking, and ran for the tree on the alert to climb up in it as the wolfhound bounded over the low gateway. At the foot of the tree she stood alert, her back arched and on the defensive. What happened next was as amazing as the levitation of the tumbler which had contained the lethal draught of crushed capsules. Nancy related so graphically how the dog's spirit and behaviour changed as from the moment it was over the gate and saw the cat by the tree. Instead of dashing in its direction he went forward towards it, not too quickly, wagging his tail. The cat's back ceased to arch itself. She remained where she was, allowing the dog to approach. The dog went straight

146

up to the cat and the cat, apparently unsurprised and no longer afraid, returned his demonstration of new-found affection. She rubbed herself up against the dog and the dog licked her fur, after which these two formerly opposed creatures lay down peacefully side by side in absolute contentment. All hostility had gone and they were friends.

'As she took in this marvel the next and most transcendent of all was taking form. It was a Shape, translucent, made of light, transmitting light and clothed in garments of such pearly opalescence they would be intangible to the touch. She knew the Face. She had seen It depicted in holy pictures and upon stained glass. It was a Face which men had once seen and known and loved upon earth, and there could be no other Face like it except in Heaven. The eyes, holding such reproach, sorrow and love within their depths, were bent down upon her. The full stern lips seemed to be moving and the severity melting into such infinite gentleness that she found herself kneeling on the grass, her glad tears washing invisible holy Feet, her unbound, loosened hair drying them.

'She says the ears of her heart heard a Voice and after that the Shape seemed to ascend higher and higher skywards until it was enveloped and lost to sight amongst the ever-changing prismatic colouration that is the precursor of dawn.

'The Voice had said to her that her husband was in the garden and had a message to give to her, and now was the moment to receive it.

'She was ready, the hastened throbbing of her heart sounding like muffled drums in her ears.

'She had risen to her feet, perfectly certain now that he had been enabled by supernal means to bridge that dark chasm of bereavement for the special purpose of communication and to fill her with the faith and purpose that was to endure the full limit of her lifetime.

'The drumming ceased and her heartbeats seemed to have stopped.

'Bunny was there, as close to her as they had been in life. He was dressed in the old discarded tweed suit he had always worn when he was messing about in the garden and humming a song with the refrain to it that he was "Dan, Dan, the dustbin man!"

'She could hardly believe that death had intervened.

' "Is it really you, my darling?" Her whole being throbbed with rejoicing.

'And his reply: "Of course. I'm here. I'm with you. Make sure of it."

'She was folded in his arms. Her hands touched and felt the tangible texture of his tweed coat. Her face was pressed against the material and she breathed in the smoky aroma of its heather and peat mixture looming and mingling with the brand of Honey Dew tobacco he had always smoked.

'She snuggled close to him.

' "Is nothing changed? Have you come to fetch me? Don't let me be sad and missing you any more!"

'His reply: "Everything is vastly changed, naturally. I was in another dimension, but it's wonderful. It will take me a thousand ages to get back, but that will only seem like a moment gone as it says in the hymn. I haven't come to fetch you, not yet. I have been permitted to come to tell you."

' "To tell me what?"

' "Just this. Not to be a little fool. Your job is to spend all the rest of your life helping the helpless here within your sphere."

' "But I don't understand—"

148

' "You will understand. I must go now, my darling. Never have any more doubts, will you?"

' "But helping people? Is that all?"

' "Isn't that everything? Promise me you will carry on."

' "I promise."

' "That's my girl." (Exactly as he would have spoken in life!) "I must be off now."

' "Bunny! When – when shall I see you again?"

' "Not in this life, I'm afraid, because it's different where I am. There's no clock-time. You will know all about that one day, and it's so easy to adjust, so perfectly simple, only on such a magnificent scale. No more muddled thinking or conjectures. Simple arithmetic. Science. The Cosmos. Astronomy isn't complicated. Neither are dimensions once one has got the hang of them. The long and the short of them isn't addition, multiplication, subtraction, decimals or fractions. It just boils down to the figure One. God. Got that, my darling? Don't let anything confuse you. Just keep your promise to carry on."

' "Before you go – tell me what you are doing now?"

'She received her answer.

' "What do you expect? What else should I be given to do except what I have loved to do most? The same for all of us. For me, it's painting. Painting all your colours on earth though, maybe, when I'm good enough I may be transferred to the farthest stars, but not until you come. I am painting with the brushes you put into my hands, but they've been transformed, as the poet Kipling described it, from sable into brushes of comet's hair. Think of it, my precious! And now get back to your little bed, my love, and don't be lonely any more".'

25

FRIEDA's description of the mystical but entirely real experience vouchsafed to her closest woman friend and confided to her only, had held Gerard enthralled as he listened. It was so naturally told that it might have been given to him at first-hand by the recipient herself.

'Do you think all this was only Nancy's imagining?' she asked him, 'Or can you believe that it is true? You don't think that grief threw her off her balance? I can assure you she is one of the most balanced persons I know.'

He had already made up his mind on that point.

'I feel absolutely convinced that it happened.'

She was satisfied.

'I felt that you would, or I could not have said so much, and now I would like to say a little more concerning Nancy.'

'Please do. I would very much like to meet her. And her life as she carries on with it today, does it satisfy her entirely?'

'It is her life, her whole life. It is the ladder of light by which she has to climb into the perfect day when she again meets her dear one. She is perfectly satisfied and now she would not have it otherwise. She does not even feel that he is near to her since that time! She knows that she has to find the way to him, and that where he is there will also be work for her. She lives now by faith.'

'Tell me something more about her work.'

'I would like to. There are so many things, some big and some small. You could fill a separate book with her doings, but make it a digression if you like within this history of my so far less important life of which at the least I can say, I also have tried to do my best and not to live to satisfy my own conceits or selfishnesses. Some of her works have become known and wherever she goes she is approved, but it is not approval or even gratitude that she looks for. Her ascent up the ladder skywards makes her quite unconscious of anything of that kind. All that she does amongst humble persons in her immediate vicinity is so quietly performed that it does not travel around. Only I, myself, have known of these small deeds, the ministrations no one else would conceive to carry out as a duty.'

'Such as?'

'One was a very old, old woman who was so weary and weak she could scarcely drag herself out of bed to do her small amount of cleaning and cooking, but she would not let anyone know she was in need of assistance because she was afraid she might be taken away by authority to some kind of institution for the infirm as she has no relatives to look after her. She was an indomitable old soul and she had struggled on in spite of age and infirmity to keep her home. Nancy, the Little Mother, after she became aware of her need, used to get up early and be out in her little car to be there first thing, by seven o'clock every morning, to bring the old woman her cup of tea and light her kitchen fire for her. Later in the day she would be with her again taking her a cooked meal, and then clean around and bring in sticks and coal. This she did for many months until the old woman died.

'Then there was another instance of the sad infirmity of old age. This one was an old man, a widower, whose wife had died recently and he was grief-stricken and bereft. For many years he had been crippled with arthritis. Now that she was gone, although the cemetery was a good distance from where he lived he had made the gallant attempt to visit her grave and place flowers upon it until at last he was unable to, and his limbs would not take him as far as his own front door. He had a bad fall and must remain in his chair. His doctor had told him he could not expect to improve. One day this good Samaritan found him weeping, and when she knew the reason for his tears from then on she took over that loving service on his behalf, regularly once a week, and kept the grave tidy.'

'What else? So much else. She makes it part of her routine to visit an institution for stray dogs and to install these poor creatures who remain unclaimed in the happy kennels she keeps at Dream Cottage, with the roving woods for dog's delight and exercise that stretch beyond. She visits the Catholic convent in Los Angeles where young girls under seventeen, in need of care and attention, have been placed under the jurisdiction of the Mother Superior and the Sisters of Carmel. After a probationary period they are allowed a certain amount of liberty and then they frequently abscond. It is the moment for which so many are planning and watching and waiting. Nancy makes herself responsible for some of the wildest ones. She has special afternoons and evenings set aside when they are invited to Dream Cottage, and they can have music and dancing and even bring their boy friends provided they are not rowdy and behave themselves.

'She visits a home known as Overton for mentally depressed cases or incurable alcoholics. Some of these forlorn persons have no one to visit them, so that their sense of isolation must be very depressing and unpleasant. What does Nancy do? She finds out who are these unfortunates. She calls in on them regularly on visiting day and they look forward to her coming and know that they have a friend. There is one poor fellow in particular whose brain became partly damaged through a mining accident and nothing can be done for him. He has lost his speech, but his eyes can speak. I have been to the home with her and seen and discovered for myself what she does for him. She launders his handkerchiefs! Yes, my friend, just that. It may seem trivial but you see, this makes that part of his poor mind that is so gratified with small things feel that he has someone who cares for him, so each week she returns to him the clean ones and he has ready for her the ones she will take away. The look on his face of childish pleasure when she handed him the little parcel of clean handkerchiefs and he undid it and saw the sprigs of lavender out of her garden she had placed in between, I shall not forget.

'Small things? How small would you say they are? Not small to the One who knows when a sparrow falls or the exact number of hairs in our heads.

'Before I finish I must tell you the last deed that was in its final stage of satisfaction and encouragement just before I came away to England.

'It is the story of a bad boy who was known as Bat's Ears, but he is not called that any more. It is not now descriptive of the bad lad who is no longer bad and whose real name is Colin. You see, Bat's Ears was the nick-name he had been given ever since he was small because that is how they stuck out, and he was jeered at and taunted by his schoolmates, girls as well, who when they saw him approaching would call to each other "Here comes Bat's Ears". The boys would tweak his ears and the girls would run away. Then he began to play truant from school and to become involved in fights for the sheer provocation caused by the derision over his name. How could he help having ears like a bat and why wasn't he like the rest with ordinary ears, ears to hear with, set close to the head and not huge and protruding to make him a figure of fun? He became worse and grew into a bad boy, to lie and to thieve until he was a real young thug with a flick knife and a razor blade he didn't use for shaving. He hadn't quite arrived at the shaving stage, but his face was covered with an unbecoming down. He shambled like a monkey when he walked, his arms dangling loosely. His parents turned him out. They could do nothing with him. Soon there followed his appearance before a Juvenile Court for a brawl and misdemeanour. Nancy was present. Nancy made herself responsible for him and brought him to Dream Cottage, where she gave him a partitioned off space with a skylight up in the loft for a bedroom, which pleased him very much, but he didn't thank her. He only mumbled and grunted, but he loved brushing and combing and exercising her family of stray dogs. I expect that is what he felt like himself.

'I had just gone to live with her at Dream Cottage in those days and that was when I first saw him. I told Nancy I thought he might be dangerous. She only smiled in her sweet way. She hadn't even attempted to take away his queer armoury of flick knife, razor blade and a knotted arrangement of string he called his duster.

At last, by the secret ways that were particularly hers for never seeming to blame anyone who was thought to be anti-social in the way he was, asking questions which brought her nearer to the painful spot as a doctor investigates hurts by his method of probing with his fingers, she discovered the root-cause of his grievance against all his fellows and girls as well, except one pin-up he had over his bed of Marilyn Munroe, who was then at her zenith as a rave.

'The grievance was his awful ears. He had come to see himself as a monstrosity like the Beast in the fairy tale. Once he confessed to Nancy he had tried to cut them off, but it had hurt too much and ears bleed such a lot. He gave up the effort after he had nicked the lobe of one ear. No, these ears would have to remain fixed to his head for life. He became sullen and wicked-thinking, hating everybody.

'Nancy has a very great friend, who is also a very good man. Besided being a distinguished surgeon who performs the finest plastic operations in surgery, he is an altruist. She told him of the lad's bad history and malformation and took him for an opinion and an examination. I am now at the end of my story. Dr. Cutler, free of charge and for the one benevolent purpose of combining with Nancy to help this bad lad to redeem himself, performed the delicate operation and plastic manipulation by grafting which made the ears resembling a bat's into well-shapen ears, set close to the head.

'Plastic surgery operations do not always take very long to become effective. Within thirty days Colin was transformed. When the bandages were taken from his head he was astonished. His whole attitude was changed from his walk to his manner. Bat's ears? He held himself erect. He took the down off his face and Nancy, one day leading him to the mirror, announced: "Colin, look at yourself. You are a fine-looking young man. You are tall and you are well-shaped and strong and your ears look lovely. You can do anything. You can go anywhere, meet people, show yourself and make me proud of you, will you?"

And Colin did.

'He is now a newly discovered person to himself, a diligent

student working in a scientist's laboratory where plastic surgery is his chief study. His aim is to become a practitioner.

'So now you must understand what the Little Mother does as she mounts upwards on that so fluctuating, narrow ladder of light which is planted in the shifting soil of earth and reaches so high that its topmost rung is behind the sky.'

26

FRIEDA'S air-passage already arranged, the days before she must fly away were running so short so that now, when Gerard was with her, there was little opportunity for any conversation other than this life-history she was relating to him up to the point of its unpredictable conclusion. As soon as he was installed in the armchair facing her and had filled his pipe from the tin of tobacco she now always kept at hand especially for him, she was ready to continue her flow of reminiscence.

'How long did I remain with my sister-friend, the Little Mother, Nancy Dean at Dream Cottage? For several weeks, doing nothing whatever except to laze and lie about in the garden in a special hammock she had fixed for me, and when I was inclining to doze, smelling in the sweet scents and listening to all the nature sounds of the bees humming, grass-hoppers chirping and birds singing, I had the lovely sensation that I was suspended between earth and heaven. My ears were so delicately attuned that I felt I could almost hear the fluttering of the butterfly's wings. She insisted that I must not try to hasten my complete recovery. I must just allow it to happen.

'As I grew stronger I felt I was striking roots in that lovely home of hers in which there was such an atmosphere of love. Would I ever wish to return to the unrewarding crowd-work in the film studios with its underworld night-life which one could not be in the company of its denizens by day without being aware of? It was not so much like that in the British Studios. Over here in England the tired-out workers go to bed early so as to be up early though still tired, and the drug and vice-traffic, the Saturnalian orgies which take place around Los Angeles are only looked upon as highly exaggerated fantasies; but they are actual shabby and depraved facts upon which the down-town population of Los Angeles flourishes and exists.

'At this time in these peaceful and health-recreating surroundings of affection and sympathy, my professional ambitions to be an artist in dramatic expression went into some kind of eclipse. I thought if I could be active in helping Nancy I might find the satisfaction everyone of us needs in doing something which brings good results, and I discussed this new outlet with her when I felt my energy was becoming renewed and it was no longer enough to be such an inactive passenger. I wanted to be of real help to her and co-operate in her work if she would allow me.

' "I have been considering all this," she said.

' "You must have something to do, but it should be creative. I have been talking to Herman about you. It's time you knew him and I shall arrange it. He is the one person who will know exactly what you should do and whatever advice he gives you, you should take."

' "Who is this Herman, and why should he know better than anyone else?" I asked.

' "Because he is a very exact person. His mind works that way. He is a perfectionist, a precision artist and a genius. He is the greatest producer we have in Hollywood today. He first made his name in the silent pictures and he has maintained it ever since. As well as that he is a good man, an inspired altruist. Money can't buy him. He is an independent producer. He was one of Bunny's greatest and closest friends. You haven't met him before because he's only just returned from working on a picture in Iceland and now he tells me he will be starting on another almost at once. A very big subject, a masterpiece, he describes it – the picture he says he has been waiting to make all his life. We shall hear all the details when we see him on Sunday. He will be coming back here to lunch after the service at our Church, for he is a Catholic as we are. Of course he was most interested when I told him I had you staying with me, not only because you are my new-found little sister, but the same nationality as himself and the daughter of Nemo."

'Herman von Hutteroth! The truly inspired producer who gave to me the supreme chance of my life, is still continuing to keep on the highest level of the producer's art. Never has he been known to sacrifice his artistic integrity to the dictators of the movie industry whose clutching fingers only release the money-bags to fill them twice over again. What a privilege and an honour to have worked under his imaginative direction! I owe everything to him, everything that I am today. He is an old man now, but still as full of zest for his work and inspired with the high purpose that drives him.

'Proud of his German ancestry and the "von" before his name – which is to be found in the *Almanach de Gotha* – he has never changed his nationality. Immediately one comes into contact with him, the impression of his strong personality is felt. He is electrical, a smallish, quickly moving, quickly thinking human dynamo with the wide stride of a sailor when he moves over the studio as if it were a ship's deck, and he the captain of the vessel. His features are sharp, aquiline. He wears a monocle without affectation but in the same manner as a necessary adjunct to his weaker eye as the late George Arliss, one of those most unforgettable performances he directed. His forehead is as lofty as his great ideals and the red-grey, short-cut hair, more grey nowadays than before, is inclined to stand up aggressively *en brosse*. He has a voice of gold, a most fabulous voice. He does not need to raise it. He never raves or shouts, jumps or stamps or flies into frenzies. The golden voice compels. He never uses a megaphone. He can pitch it with the surest measure of acoustics to reach the farthest corner of the studio. If he had chosen to be an actor he could himself have essayed the greatest rôles.

'My first meeting with him at that lunch-time and then afterwards when lunch was over, I expect, she absented herself on purpose in her thoughtfulness for me that Herman von Hutteroth and I should have a conversation by ourselves, Nancy went out in her car to take some food to the old widower of whom I have already spoken. For nearly an hour this great producer conversed with me and all that he said was of the greatest weight and importance. The tenor of his conversation was as if already, although I was no one, he considered me as an artist.

'All the time we were talking, although I was not conscious of it for I was too absorbed in what he was telling me to consider if I was making any impression on him, he must have been observing me with his acute producer's perception. He passed on lastly to the subject of the picture he was going to make which was filling him with eagerness and enthusiasm to commence. Of course everybody has heard of "The Eagle and the Cross", the film of the novel by Carl Bernard. The book had only recently been published at that time but at once it became famous for the style of the author and its so unusual story which Herman von Hutteroth then told me and said I must read immediately. The film rights had been sold upon publication. He would send me a copy.

'It is a story so simply told that it does not seem intricate or impossible, although its theme is war, death and re-incarnation. He described it as it would be presented in the film where first, before anything comes up on the screen, there is heard the most beautiful choral singing of the nuns at their evening service in their chapel, and then coming out of the empty screen and projected forwards into full focus, the Holy Cross and superimposed against this, both in sound and sight, the steady drone of approaching air-craft engines and, sweeping across the sky above the Cross, five aircraft in formation. Fade out of the sound and the Holy Cross to the unfolding of the tale itself. Such a mystical, reverent theme which is dated in the period of the First World War and is concerned with a young novice of a not so strictly enclosed order. Her meeting just outside the convent grounds is with a young German ace pilot-officer of the calibre of a Richthoven, whose fighter squadron is based near by. He sees her first at service and she forgets her custody of the eyes. She falls in love with him and knows that she cannot complete her novitiate to be a bride of Christ. He is shot down and killed. She forsakes the Convent and returns to a secular life of false gaieties and abandon-ment. She grows older into the fifties, but remains beautiful as a full-blown rose, the favourite of millionaires and men of position and title. On board a liner proceeding from New York she makes acquaintance with an inspired young evan-gelist into whom the spirit of the brave German Ace was reborn immediately upon his death. No longer the Eagle who fought in the skies, he serves the Cross, his mission to redeem and save.

'In a most solemn and mystical scene between them these two persons of such diverse ages, he now, in his re-incarnated life young enough to be her son, both become aware of their former state of being when they had held their lovers' meetings in secret and she had stolen out of the convent to be with him.

'Now, it is his mission to redeem her and her's the new-found penitence and resolve of a Magdalene to retrace her steps along the paths of devotion and sanctity. The finale is reached when the young evangelist and his convert to-gether visit the graveside of the former German ace in France where the burial ground with its many wooden crosses is within the sight of the convent. In his clerical dress he stands at the salute looking up at the sky against which a cross is forming and she kneels and prays while, as in the opening shot, the notes of an organ rise and swell and the sweet voices of the nuns at their evening service are heard chanting the triumphant *Te Deum*.

'After he had described all this in detail Herman von Hutteroth sat stroking his chin and staring at me intently as if he was having a close-up taken of me, then he said:

' "The rôle of Walter Holz, the fighter-pilot, is already contracted for to be played by Max Romer. He is such a box-proposition the backers insist their choice is final, and even I, who have my wishes considered in most cases, am obliged to bend to their decree although I consider he is unfit by his own nature to assume a character of such fineness and bravery."

'He continued thoughtfully to speak what he was con-sidering in his mind.

' "But Marguerite, the novice, the postulant, the choice

162

and the risk could be for me if I desire to take it upon
my shoulders to discover the new star, and I think, little
one, *liebschen*, her Neon name is Frieda Bloch, the
daughter of my compatriot, Nemo, the *auguste* of the circus
ring.'''

27

' T H I S that I am going to tell you about – what chapter is it you will be putting on record when you click on your typewriter this evening? – Twenty-seven? Then this one to come is the happiest, most complete, satisfying, exciting, stimulating, and rewarding passage in my life.

'This superb production in which I had been lifted out of obscurity to play Marguerite de Beauregard, the novice, that made modern film history due to the faultless inspired direction of Herman von Hutteroth as he interpreted and entered into the inner mind of the author who first conceived it as a novel, conferred on me such joy that it is almost impossible to explain.

'In every aspect it was colour and harmony he strove for and attained from everyone within that enormous studio space including the step-up clapper boys, studio workmen, scenery pushers, camera-men, electricians, monitor men, mike monkeys to the motion-picture actors themselves, extras and bit-parters included. In spite of movement, bustle, hammering, the noises of assembly and preparation except for the quietness and dead silence when actual scenes were being shot, that floor space might have been within a cathedral where rehearsals were taking place for some significant ceremony to come.

'Harmony, conformity, and respect and observance with one exception. This spirit was absent in one person only, the big box office magnet film-star, Max Romer, who would arrive driving himself in his fabulous low-built, stream-lined, long-nosed racing model car, white painted with scarlet lines and upholstery of white bearskin. Fabulous is a word very much over-used, most particularly by those in the film-world, but suitable enough for the car of an exhibitionist such as Max Romer.

'His name and his appearance are familiar to all, of course. There is no one who can equal him for his handsome Nordic looks, his fairness, physique and assurance; and he is undisputably a fine and sure artist. The direction of Herman von Hutteroth he never questioned or disputed. His own artistry responded and reacted immediately to deliver exactly what was required of him. The arrogance that streamed from him off the set was as much a part of himself as the exaggerated cut of his clothes, the suits of Hollywood tailoring built up to accentuate the lines of his god-like figure. He also possesses a curious undulating grace of carriage accompanied with certain gesticulations which seem to hint at the effeminate in contradiction to his *beau sabreur* aspect. He had scarcely seemed to notice me except to kiss my hand when I was anywhere near to him. Outside the studios while the production was in progress I never saw him, because in the early morning Nancy would drive and leave me there in her car and fetch me away in the evening, insisting that I went to bed and had my supper brought up to me so that I should have the fullest rest. It was an exacting rôle for one so young as I to play, first as the pure and innocent young novice, and then after a gap of years to the changed, ageing woman, the full-blown rose in a section of the degenerate society into which she had drifted after she had forsaken the convent.

'I was completely absorbed in what I was doing. I lived

it and even in my sleep I was dreaming the character I was portraying.

'It was when we were in the Fresno Valley on location. It had been chosen because of its likeness to Flanders, its smiling vineyards and poplars and suitability for the flying scenes where was built an exact replica of a German fighter squadron of the First War, even to obtaining the very aircraft of that historic time. Built up also, and appearing most realistic and substantial, were the convent and clustering little whitewashed cottages and villas with red roofs.

'In no scene where there were flying risks to be taken was Max Romer involved. He had never been a flier and in any case apart from the scene in which, as the fighter-ace, he had to be pursued and shot down in a dog-fight above the clouds, those scenes in which he was actually seen in the cockpit were a ply-wood mock-up in the studio against which was superimposed a backcloth of moving clouds which were manufactured of heated steam blown up through gratings in the background. The actual fighting scene in the air was performed by a team of practised dare-devils who risk their lives in all manner of film stunts because they enjoy doing it as well as the very big money they earn. They even crack jokes amongst themselves as to which hospital they prefer.

'The stunt-flier engaged to double for Max Romer was an aerobatic expert whose speciality was combat tactics of that very period, which he had studied in exactly the same way as a master fencer studies the tactics of a sixteenth-century swordsman. In fact, after I came to know him so very well indeed, which is what happened, I understood how the absorption of his life was concerned with the air and every-thing that has to do with flying.

'His name was Teddie Hamilton and he was to be very soon my second husband. It all came about very suddenly, as in my life all events of the greatest significance and importance seem to have happened.

'The first time I saw him was when he was taxi-ing his machine right up to the camera-line upon the tar-mac. Immediately the cameras in my eyes took the close-up of his dark brown wind-blown hair, his open countenance with lips that seemed to be smiling even if they were un-parted and he was not laughing, and his alive humorous eyes with the look of the wide horizon in them which is in the eyes of the men who go down to the sea in ships or travel the skies.

'The first words I heard him speak were those he called out to the camera-man: "Okay that time, or do you want me to do the whole circuit? I don't mind. I don't have to pay for the gas, you know! Come on, boys. You can't send me often enough. It's my delight up in the skies. Why don't you sample it, you groundlings!"

'The camera-man assured him that last shot was fine. Teddie them climbed out of the plane and, as his feet reached the ground, he looked straight at me with a smile as wide as his eyes and waved his hand towards me before he turned and walked away in the direction of the sheds. It was a salutation which rang an immediate bell in me.

'Everything now was destined to happen in that speeded-up fashion which seems to follow upon any long pause in our existence where there has been a lull or a period of suspension such as that peaceful restorative interval while I was convalescent and cared for by my little sister-mother at her home.

'Instantly I knew in that lightning-flash of perception which can pass between two opposites, I had seen someone

167

who was to be, and who was already, of tremendous significance for me, and from whom I would not wish to depart, nor he from me, so long as we could remain in orbit together, though one might be hurled into the nothingness of a dark ocean of conjecture and the other to wonder and hope, to despair and finally to become resigned to the silence of no return.

'This comes later, soon enough, too soon.

'Later on that same afternoon when work on the set had ended for that day and all but a few had already left, and while Herman von Hutteroth and those he had need of were in the projection room viewing the last rushes, I was waiting to be fetched by Nancy who had not yet arrived. Max Romer, whom I had not thought was still upon the premises, came down the stairs from the dressing rooms. My mind was still deeply engrossed and I could only think of the stunt-flier who had waved his hand at me as if recognizing a familiar figure after returning from some prodigiously long flight outside this existence; so when Max Romer accosted me I scarcely seemed to be aware of what he was saying, which was an invitation to drive back with him to the fabulous house in Hollywood he was renting for those few weeks, to dine with him and afterwards to familiarise ourselves with those as yet unrehearsed scenes of the close-ups, that were to be taken tomorrow of the intimate scences between the novice and the war-ace in the film. He said he wished to help me, particularly as these would be of such a delicate nature that, as I was inexperienced in that line of film acting, I might quite naturally feel embarrassed under the cameras at such near range unless I had some knowledge of what was expected of me.

'How could I doubt his honesty of purpose? His manner

was pleasantly impersonal and re-assuring, so if I had had any doubts they would have been dispelled.

'Nancy had still not arrived, so leaving a message with the attendant who remained on duty that she should be told not to wait and where and with whom I had gone, I stepped into his snow-white high-powered two-seater with its polar-bear lining and was driven through the exit gates swung open for us, the janitors jumping out of their boxes and saluting him as if he were a royal personage.'

28

' I MUST continue if you will bear with me. My thoughts are going ahead so fast, much faster than this film-star drove me from the studios through the traffic with such caution it almost seemed as if he was not entirely confident to handle his own magnificent car. He scarcely spoke on the way. His concentration was upon the wheel and straight ahead. We were proceeding in the direction of Santa Monica to the fashionable beach resort of Malibu with its resplendent hotels, its millionaires' houses above the beach, its homes of so many film-stars with swimming pools, and its palm trees, its bikini unclad beauties still lying late on the sands with their half-naked, bronzed-bodied male escorts stretched beside them.

'A palm-fringed drive led up to the green-roofed, fully furnished bungalow which Max Romer informed me boastfully as we came out of the car was costing him twelve hundred dollars a month. Fabulous again is the only word that is appropriate to use. He escorted me first into the sun-lounge overlooking the garden in the corner of which was set a most ostentatious cocktail bar. A Chinese man-servant appeared to take his orders for the evening meal and disappeared as silently as a genie. He told me that the services of this Chinaman as houseman-valet and his wife as cook-housekeeper were included with the exorbitant rent of his bungalow. Max Romer's humble origin from a very poor class family he never attempted to cover up. He was proud to boast of his own attainments in having left poverty so far behind.

'Going behind the cocktail bar he poured for me the orangeade with ice cubes in it I was glad to accept as I was so thirsty, and a long drink for himself. He told me to be entirely easy and relax. It had been so exceptionally hot that day in the studios.

'When we had rested he suggested it would be pleasant to rehearse the close-ups in the garden by the swimming pool where it would be cooler than indoors and we would dine afterwards. Those close-ups were of such tremendous importance, and though in these scenes I was a novice in a religious order it was essential I should be able to portray and feel the rapturous moments before abandonment which self-consciousness might ruin if buzzard-shots had to be taken because realism could not be achieved by such means. Buzzard-shots, as I expect you know, are the spoiled shots which a producer will insist must be retaken until he is satisfied.

'We were about to proceed into the garden when the unexpected arrival of some visitors who had just driven up in a car delayed us, though Max did not appear to mind. He welcomed them effusively and they all seemed on extremely affectionate terms. They were five young men dressed in gaudy floral-patterned shirts, and tight to the ankle trousers, crocodile leather sandals and extra bright socks. Their hairdressing was in various much-waved styles and dyes from ginger to black. They all had high-pitched voices and some of them lisped. Max Romer poured drinks for them and they sat about on the floor in languorous attitudes. These peculiar persons belonged to a particular colony which is well known in Hollywood of she-he's known as "the Nest". I am much wiser now than I was then.

'Eventually they left after effusive leave-takings, and calling out "Ta-ta, goodbye-ee, toodle-do, so-along" drove away waving and kissing their hands to Max, who waved and kissed his hand in response.

'Then to the swimming pool which had a Roman look with classical statues of gods and goddesses against the background of tropical foliage, pink marble pillars and a low balcony of mosaic-work and marble with garden seats and a cushioned reclining couch. In the centre of the pool was an ornamental fountain which, by pressing a knob on the balcony, he set into motion and at the same time from some hidden source soft music commenced to be played. It was a scene of enchantment, but as false as Hollywood.

'I asked Max if he enjoyed bathing in the pool and how deep was it. He said he had never tried it himself as he disliked cold water. Sometimes at the other end where it was shallow he paddled or sat and dangled his feet. The balcony side where we were was much deeper, about eight or nine feet, he made a guess. He admitted he was no swimmer. As a small child, through a boat upsetting he had been plunged into the sea and ever since he had disliked immersion. His own warm shower was how he preferred to cleanse or refresh himself.

'He invited me to have a swim first before we rehearsed, which I would have loved to do, but I had no bathing suit with me, so I refused. He said what did that matter? He would turn his back if I was shy. In any case why should anybody, whether woman or man, feel ashamed to be naked? All the Greek statues were naked or draped scantily, and the same was true of the most famous paintings of Venus beholding herself in the mirror, Juno, Aphrodite rising out of the sea, Apollo, Achilles, Eros and the rest, the un-coarsened bodies of young men being especially beautiful.

'I admitted I was shy and would prefer to rehearse straight away as that was the purpose for which he had brought me to his bungalow and I did not wish to be late returning.

'He said that would depend on how receptive I was. I was now to assume the personality of Marguerite, the postulant, stealing out into the convent grounds, tremulous with excitement and eagerness to keep her first assignment with the gallant air-ace who was impatiently awaiting her, having slipped in by the secret entrance of which she had told him.

'I must not allow myself to be startled or stiffen when I was first folded in his embrace, which, he prepared me, would be fiercely ardent because this aspect of a man's passion was impatient as many men coming out of battle and amidst the tumult are affected in such a violent manner, the behaviour of the Emperor Napoleon being one of the most striking instances of such sex-urges when he would stride forth immediately his campaign had been waged, calling out and demanding "*Une femme, une femme!*"

'I listened, but it all went over my head, and so as I made my approach with nun-like trepidation, and he, in the character of the air-ace, strode up to me and impelled me towards the cushioned couch, I was still unprepared for the brutish vehemence of his behaviour. I found myself in the embrace of a tiger, and this was more than a rehearsal for realism. It was savage, hideous, and just as I was terrifyingly aware he was mad with passion, and the true artist he was on the set now nothing more than a corrupt despoiler, I was as myself, a defenceless young girl. I could not shriek or scream. His kisses, that had nothing in them but the fierce ruthlessness of lust, were smothering me and I felt my breath leaving me. I was all but fainting or near to death. I would rather death. I was over-powered and terrified.

'Then, as I was almost losing consciousness, I heard the sound of a car approaching at speed up the drive. It stopped, a door was banged shut, someone was running up on to the balcony, and I was mercifully wrenched out of that hideous enfoldment.

'I could not move or speak; I was too shaken and weak. What followed next all took place within seconds.

'The stunt airman Teddie Hamilton was my rescuer, and that deep end of the pool so convenient. Amongst his other trick accomplishments he had Judo and even a giant of a fellow like Max could put up no resistance against that most subtle Japanese art of unarmed combat in overthrowing an adversary.

'Over the low ledge of the balcony Max was pitched headlong into the pool where it was deepest, tumbling in with a splash as huge as a whale would make.

'Teddie was now laughing and I began to recover and laugh as well, hysterical but oh! so relieved.

'Comedy had succeeded tension as on that different occasion when I had tossed those chocolates from their presentation box over the famous playwright's cabin and one of them had smashed and splashed his cheek and eye like a custard-pie.

'Max was spluttering and spitting out the pool water from his mouth after submerging. He was clinging on to the pillars of the balustrade, unable to raise himself over the ledge. I thought if he let go he might drown.

' "He can't swim. Had you not better give him a hand?"

' "Give him a hand? Not on your life! The swine's an arrant coward. Come on! Let's get you out of this! Lucky

174

I returned to the studio and the commissionaire started the ball by telling me where you'd gone. He'll soon shout! He's got lungs if he hasn't any guts. Listen! He's already started to bawl, servants will hear the blighter and drag him in and dry him. I'm driving you right home now! Darlingest, you'll have to wisen up if you're going to be a film star, or better still, let's get married at once, and I'll look after you all the time so long as I'm not away. Say 'yes' and don't think twice about it. I'm an unreliable devil, because danger is my ally, but I'm honest and I truly love you. Isn't that enough?"

'It was enough. I had known as soon as I first saw him that I should have an affinity with this fearless stunt-man who daily and hourly took his life in his hands and rejoiced most of all when he was high in the skies above the clouds and amongst the mysteries of space.'

29

'My friend, I would like to tell you so much more about Teddie, but now I am forced to compress myself as you have to, I expect, very often when you have been working late on some special and important assignment. If ever an occasion arises when I am able to return to England, and who knows that it may not be so, I could relate to you a story that would be of his adventures only, adventures all his life, because from boyhood that was his character to do and dare, until the last adventure of all which deprived me of him and which can only be guessed at in the final stages of what is now never likely to be fully-known.

'Flying was his entire life and that I accepted without any question or trying to persuade him to desist from it. He had told me of how from the day he first saw one of the earlier 'planes in the sky, he saved up his pocket-money week by week to pay for his first barn-stormer's flight in an old 'plane that seemed held together by bits of string and wire and how, during his school vacation, he prevailed upon the barn-stormer pilot to let him go up with him as some sort of an odd-job boy from village to village. He told me he never forgot those summer nights when, at the end of a long day, he would just roll up in a blanket under the wings, and then the glory of a take-off in the early dawn on to the next village. That was how he learned to fly, and by the time he was fourteen he was able to fly that old crate himself. When the Second World War broke out, he was hardly nineteen, and so what he did was to skip it to England where he joined the R.A.F. as a free-lance with that other bunch of American fliers who did the same thing. "The Hat in the Ring" squadron they were called.

'After the war he had to come back to his own territory, the same as in his adventurous boyhood, as with Bob Hope, the born comedian, successor to your own illustrious George Robey, whom the fairies at his cradle had showered with the gifts that were to make people smile and laugh, so with Teddie in his passionate zeal for dare-devil flying. He could never settle to anything else. Stunt-flying for the film studios followed because it offered all the hazards that gave him satisfaction in the elements he adored. His performances and skill came to be in constant requisition – and for excellent pay. He was very nearly satisfied. He would be off on location to wherever he might be sent and, unlike the film stars themselves, he was always to be relied upon. He neither smoked nor drank nor mixed with any of the Hollywood crowd absorbed in themselves and their own personal vanities, vices, jealousies, strifes and expenditure of physical fitness in their abandonment to empty pleasures, which shorten their own lives and involve the bank-roll men in astronomical expenditure through avoidable sicknesses caused so often through emotional disorders and indulgences. Teddie had no time for these, and for them, he who took all the risks they themselves would be scared to take even if it had been required of them, he did not exist any more than the small part people who might be beside them on the set, whom they would never deign to be aware of or to see. He despised most film-stars he said to me once because they were such trivial persons.

'Never shall I forget the one short flight I had with him in his own machine which he always attended to himself and was always assiduous to keep in first-class trim like an owner-groom the horse he rides.

'His invitation came spontaneously when he asked me if I had ever flown and I told him yes, from Germany to England, when my Bill had brought me, but never in a little plane like his.

' "Well, then," he said, "let me take you for a little flip over this incredible city. Maybe it will help you to see it in its proper perspective. I'll be very gentle with you, no stunting. Tell that little sister-in-law of yours first that you'll be coming with me and assure her that you will be perfectly safe. I like her. She's a fine little woman."

'So we fixed our flight for the next evening after the day's shooting and I had the wonderful experience of being up there in the sky with Teddie flying over the city of celluloid. Hollywood with all its garishness, had gone and, instead, I looked down upon the rolling hills slashed by the sword of the Pacific sunset, the rays of which striking the swimming pools in so many gardens turned them into ruby-red like drops of blood. The lights of the city were just coming on.

'The one and only indulgence I discovered in Teddie which he never disguised from me was his addiction for gambling. In the same way that he gambled with life he had to do it. Even an automatic slot machine would draw him to it. He expended his pay packets on playing cards for high stakes, roulette at the casino in Las Vegas, on race-horses, nearly always losing but continuing to gamble in order to recoup himself. After we were married I would gladly lend him my own money when he was so sure of a big win and anxious to repay me as well for what I had lent him before. I was never regretful that I did this, not even to this day. His big idea was to load me with all the riches he was always quite certain each time would flow in.

'We were married immediately after the film was in the can. Nancy did not attempt to dissuade me. She, too, liked Teddie very much indeed and she knew that his single hearted wish was to make me happy, as he did.

'Oh, yes, I was very happy! Life with Teddie was more like being in the company of an over-exuberant but always lovable, delighted child. He had the idea he was looking after me, but in truth it was I who was looking after him. He called forth all the maternal in me in small ways, such as tidying up after him when he quitted the bathroom leaving his toothpaste tube with the cap off rolled away somewhere to be looked for and screwed on, his pyjamas on the floor to be folded up, everything scattered, although with every tiny detail in connection with his machinery he was so tidy and meticulous.

'How much he rejoiced at the première of "The Eagle and the Cross", when I was instantly proclaimed as a film star and at certain functions I had to attend afterwards he would be with me, but always standing ever so slightly behind me like Prince Philip and Lord Snowdon when they appear in public with their royal spouses. It gave me a proud feeling to know that I was the Queen of his heart.

'My married life ended in a manner of which I had no foreboding at the time, and neither had Teddie.

'He had a friend, much older than himself, the famous explorer and archaeologist of whom everybody has heard, Houston-Mitchell, known for his knowledge and discoveries. At this time he was claiming to have located a lost city in the Matto Grosso of Brazil, which if established would throw a tremendous light on ancient civilization. To reach it overland without terrific equipment would be impossible. The first thing to do would be to establish its existence beyond all doubt. Once having done this, the necessary funds could be raised for a fully-equipped scientific expedition, and so the first step would need to be in the field of aerial survey and photography of the Lost City. Houston-Mitchell had shown Teddie the map and exact location and had sworn him to secrecy, as Colonel Fawcett extracted the same kind of promise from his wife, so that after he had departed no one knew exactly where he might be.

'The explorer had arranged for the charter of an amphibian aircraft most suitable for the flight together with photographic equipment, and his son who was a pilot, would accompany Teddie. These three were the only living men who knew what their exact destination was to be, and they set forth in high spirits upon a journey of such perils and adventures, the greatest peril of all being a forced landing in a section of jungle that would swallow an aircraft even more completely than an ocean.

'How long would they be away, I asked, when Teddie told me, not showing my heart was in my mouth. He reassured me, feeling exactly as he did over gambling, that he would win and all was in his favour. Not for me to doubt or discourage him or to beg him to stay at home. The trip should be over within a month and after that everything would be all set. Teddie told me how much he would be paid. It was a tempting sum in advance, all of which he insisted on leaving behind for me. I never touched a penny. I banked it for him to do some more gambling when he returned home. In the end I made a donation in his name for the refugees. It was the only memorial I could raise to him.

'We said goodbye. A month dragged by and there was no

communication except for one cable. What could I do? Finally I communicated with the United States Consulate in Brazil who, with the Brazilian Government, arranged an extensive search over the jungle, but it was of no avail. There has been no sign and no word to this day. That is now twelve years ago and we have been told to presume death. I had lost my Teddie, my laughing play-boy and my pal. Ever since I have carried on alone.

'Finish this chapter just here, my friend.'

30

O N her last day there was no opportunity neither was there the time to see Frieda off at the Airport, for her aircraft was scheduled to leave at ten a.m., and Gerard's own assignment for the television recorded interview of a celebrity in the political news was at the same hour and could not possibly be held up. He therefore went to her suite very early to say goodbye.

She was ready for departure, all her suitcases around her, and for the first time there was no lilac in the flower vases. Neither had he been able to bring her a bunch to put in her hands to take away with her. He had looked in early at the florist's shop to be informed by the blonde sales-girl: 'No lilacs for you today. There won't be any more now till next Spring.'

As he came into the lounge of her suite she had been looking into the mirror and he saw what she was doing, she was leaning forward and pushing up the corners of her mouth.

When she turned from it to him, she was smiling.

A hotel-attendant was just behind Gerard:

'Your taxi is at the door, madame.' He took her suitcases.

'I've run it very fine. I tried to get here earlier but I was delayed by a press call.' Gerard could not disguise that he was feeling solemn.

They were alone for those few moments.

The smile, like everything she performed, even if it was only an act, was an achievement.

'It doesn't matter. It is perhaps better this way that we do not draw it out with any regrets. We have no regrets to look back upon. That is something alone to be grateful for. Think of what I shall be going to do as soon as I am on Broadway rehearsing. After all this time there is to be a stage version of "The Eagle and the Cross". My loveliest part of all, and if it is to be my Swansong, who knows, what a song it will be, what an expression and what a fulfilment. After that I may allow myself to rest and obey the doctor's instructions. What is this?'

He was holding out a half-sheet of notepaper he had taken from his wallet.

'Some lines I wrote especially for you last night – just as they came to me. I hadn't the time to type them.'

'May I read now?'

'Please do. There are only a very few.'

She read the lines slowly aloud, her voice low-pitched but vibrant with feeling, putting into the words their fullest meaning.

' "This most delicate goblet
Of flawless crystal is fragile.
We will treat it with love and care
One abrupt movement of your hand or mine
Could turn this lovely thing into a thousand splinters
And the small swords of glass
Pierce deep wounds into our hearts.
Such treasure is not for desecration
This goblet is for precious wine."

'Thank you. I shall keep these for always. The lilac may fade, but the lovely words remain.' She kissed the half-page and slipped it into her bag.

Still she continued to smile though her eyes were misty, with stars behind them.

'Now let us make our farewell in the German way. In the English way also, which may be romantic, but never theatrical. If a break has to be made, we make it a break though we hope and pray it may be otherwise when we are parting from someone dear. I hope you have great satisfaction in your future. If she is not to be me who will be beside you, I hope she may be a better, finer person than I am. In loving kindness we have to part, and to live as well as we can. There come into my mind some words my old refugee German friend who was a distinguished psychologist taught to me from the saying of a philosopher who lived in the B.C. era when men seemed most incredibly wiser than we in this age, because we are all so speeded up we have so little time to pause and think. This quotation: *He alone seems to me to live and to enjoy existence, who intent upon any business, seeks fame by some distinguished action or honourable art* – which means that we have our work to do and in doing it we may be happy. *Liebe wohl*, my dear, dear friend! My taxi may wait, but the aeroplane will not.'